Hippocrates (c 460 – c 370BC), an
is traditionally regarded as the Fatl
as a 'guide to conduct' by the medi
ages and still used in the graduation
schools.

CW00548011

In the Hippocratic Oath (not to be confused with "Hypocritical Oaf!") it pledges to prescribe only beneficial treatments, according to his abilities and judgement, to refrain from causing harm or hurt, to live an EXEMPLARY personal and professional life – GULP!

The years from my first day at Medical School (1967) to my last day in General Practice (1995) were largely dominated by extremely hard work and punishingly long hours. However, I have always felt blessed to have studied and practiced medicine and to have had often unlimited access to the personal lives of many of my patients. That clearly was a great privilege. However, my nature has always been mischievous which I hope comes across in many of my recollections of that period. I have, on the whole, managed to keep out of trouble, although on some occasions have come pretty close. Of course, there are countless serious and sometimes tragic circumstances that I have shared with patients of which I have also touched upon in my stories.

Would I have enjoyed practising medicine in the last 30 years as I did in the preceding period of time? Probably not – as I sure as hell don't enjoy being a patient!

Rod Brooks.

This book is dedicated to our
lovely long-suffering wives

Louise and Frances

Sex Drugs and General Practice

Dr Rod Brooks and Dr Duncan Stewart

Contents

Dr D – FAMILY MATTERS

Once I had abandoned the ambition to be a train driver, after a brief flirtation with the idea of becoming a sauce chef, I decided at the age of about 10 to become a doctor. In my family, there was a high level of approval for the medical profession as my paternal grandfather had been a GP. His older son went into medical research and eventually became a Professor of Pharmacology, having been advised to quit the arduous life of a GP after he suffered a stroke in his late 20s. He was very peripherally connected to Fleming's discovery of Penicillin at St Mary's Hospital. My mother's younger brother, Duncan who she adored, was a vet. After the war, he undertook haematological research in Iraq and then departed for Adelaide, Australia after being refused a renewal of his UK passport on the basis that he did not have a male forbear born in the UK during the previous century. This was true as they, like him and my mother, had all been born in Chile. He could have been forgiven for assuming that surviving four years as a navigator, flying in Mosquitoes for the RAF, would have qualified him for UK citizenship.

My grandfather practised in Barnet, and was by all accounts a kind, skilful physician who was much loved by his patients and his family. I have memories from when I was about six of him sitting in a high-backed armchair wearing a velvet smoking jacket, flannel trousers, grey suede brogues and smoking Passing Cloud cigarettes, which came in a pink box. He and my grandmother lived in a large house that included a billiards room and its own tennis court. The gardener's wife was the cook, and they had a maid called Mary, who was devoted to my grandfather. Mary had come to see him at the age of 18 in a very distressed state. She had been sacked by her employer, a disastrous event in those days as it made it almost impossible for her to get a reference for a new position. Her previous employer mistrusted all his staff and would test their honesty by leaving money around. Mary, who was quite a feisty young woman, became so angry at being treated like this that the next time she found a "mislaid" half sovereign she nailed it to the mantelpiece, and was immediately dismissed. My grandfather employed her on the spot, and she stayed with the family for nearly 60 years.

His brother Percy was an even more successful businessman than their illustrious father, who had founded The London Brick Company, and was very generous to his siblings, all of whom received, among other things, a Rolls Royce. The car was something of an embarrassment for my grandfather.

One Sunday afternoon my father, aged about four, overheard a phone call requesting an urgent visit. My father swung into action and, when his father emerged from the house, he found his son enthusiastically emptying the contents of a watering can into the petrol tank.

You can understand a son's adoration for a man whose response was to thank him for being so helpful and pat him on the head.

My father suffered several severe childhood illnesses, which left him a sickly child, blind in one eye and emotionally insecure by the time he went as a boarder to Belmont Prep School in Mill Hill. However, by the time he left the senior school 10 years later, he was an excellent gymnast, a member of the Rugby Football First XV and had secured a place at Cambridge University to read Modern Languages.

When he was demobbed in 1946, as a married man with me and my mother to support, work was hard to find. So, he accepted a job in Stoke-on-Trent as the editor of a scientific journal publishing research papers on ceramics. Sadly, he never took to Stoke. He worked very hard but had no real enthusiasm for his work and I was always aware of this anxiety about money. My school fees were in part paid for by my grandfather but were still a considerable burden for my parents.

Mill Hill had a Medical Sixth Form, which I entered after doing my "O" levels; two years later, I left with three "A" levels, a requirement that enabled me to skip the first year of medical study when I headed for Guy's Hospital Medical School.

Dr R – A TEN-YEAR SENTENCE

When I was 10 years old, I was an extremely fit young man who had never had a day's illness up until then. I was attending a state primary school in Hove, East Sussex. My classmates and I were all somewhat anxious, as we had recently taken our 11+ Examination, the results of which were due imminently. A pass would take us to the local grammar school with an opportunity to take "O" Levels, then "A" Levels and on to university. Then the world would be our oyster, our form master promised us. A failure would dump us (his words) into a Secondary Modern School where you could stop dreaming, unless you wanted to be a footballer or a rock star, which was, of course, what most of us wanted to be anyway! I went on to pass and the rest is history. However, before that happened, I developed severe stomach pains on my lunch break, which I went home for, as I lived so close to the school. By the time my class was dismissed for the day, I had been carted off to the Royal Alexandra Hospital for sick children, a couple of miles away. By this time, I was feeling pretty rough and had thrown up twice in the ambulance, which didn't make me very popular. The children's doctor made a diagnosis of acute appendicitis. Four hours later, I was being operated on to remove the offending inflamed appendix. I awoke and thought I was in heaven. The prettiest nurse, with the most wonderful foreign accent (I was later to learn that Nurse Bethan was Welsh) was holding my hand. My heart was racing so much that the doctor in the recovery unit intervened. He was concerned enough to monitor me on an ECG machine for the next hour. It finally all settled down after she had left the recovery room to attend to another child. I was seven days in the children's ward getting over the operation. Twice a day this lovely young beauty came to see me and held my hand while she took my temperature and pulse. She was always a little concerned with the latter, but I was beginning to manage to control it better. When I was told that I was well enough to go home it was Bethan's day off and I mourned that I would never see her again. Six long weeks later, my Mum took me back to the Royal Alexandra for a post-op check-up. In the outpatient waiting room, she walked by and smiled at me. I have never forgotten that moment in my life, even though it was 64 years and four months ago as I write. What I learnt from it was what gentle kindness can do to a vulnerable patient in a strange bed. I decided there and then that I wanted to be just like her… well not quite just like her; I now wanted to be a male nurse. (Twenty years later, I nearly did that, but I got close enough.)

In 1967, I applied to Charing Cross Hospital Medical School in London to train to become a doctor, having been talked out of being a policeman by my father (a retired Superintendent of Sussex Police Force). My father was a career policeman, and did very well, considering he came from working class roots and resisted the temptation of becoming a freemason. At the time, this could considerably enhance one's career prospects. He retired after 32 years' service as a Superintendent and worked for the rest of his life as a Registrar of Births, Deaths and Marriages. I was very proud of his achievements and loved the drama of him rushing out in the middle of the night in an unmarked police car to some incident or other. I wanted to follow in his footsteps, but he felt that I had greater opportunities, so medicine seemed the obvious choice, as it was both vocational and chaotic!

I would also have liked to be a professional footballer, having played in goal for Brighton and Sussex Schoolboys, but the call never came. Cambridge University would have been my first choice but, as a grammar school lad, I didn't have the confidence to apply. One of the boys I sat next to at school went on to captain his side in top-flight English Football (the old First Division now renamed The Premier League). He married young, retired in his early thirties, retrained as a solicitor, and joined his wife in a legal firm. I felt he achieved the best of both worlds: he was a sportsman and an academic, and he managed to keep to one wife! The best of THREE worlds perhaps!

Having been offered a conditional place at medical school, I had to rearrange my "A" levels as I was studying physics, chemistry, pure math, and applied math. I thought I was really good at arithmetic, but I didn't make the intellectual transition from "O" level to "A" level. With great relief, I dropped the two maths subjects and replaced them with biology. This fulfilled the requirement for the Charing Cross entrance exam.

I remember the day I was offered a place at medical school. My father took me to the local mortuary to confront me with the body of a young woman who had fallen asleep at the driving wheel of her car. She had had an accident, and subsequently died. I think he was genuinely surprised that I took the experience in my stride. Little did I know that, only 10 years later I would be looking at my father on the same mortuary table. He had died unexpectedly of a heart attack at the age of 60. Sadly, it was the fate of many retired police officers of his generation.

I fell in love for the first time during my sixth form years: a complication that didn't help my grades. However, we both muddled through our studies. Heather became a junior schoolteacher in the East End of London. We married a couple of years later and had our first child, Ben, while I was still at medical school.

In my teens, I fancied myself as a footballer, my position being a goalkeeper and occasional centre forward. Disappointingly, I did not get an England schoolboys' cap, but my football abilities featured heavily in my interview for entrance into Charing Cross Hospital Medical School. I was offered a place and, on my first day, the Vice-Dean came up to me. "You are Brooks, the goalkeeper, aren't you?" Charing Cross was the smallest medical school by far, 45 students per year in comparison to Barts' and St Thomas's intake of around 100 per year. However, we went on to win the Inter-London Medical School Knock-out Football Cup two years in a row. Not sure how the selection system works now. We recently had a 50-year reunion of our successful football squad. We are all alive, and all Grammar-School-educated; and there are four professors among us, (not including me!) I asked them what they would have liked to do if they had not become doctors.

Three of us (including me) replied "footballers!" What a loss to the Premier League, I thought. My father-in-law, Bill, also influenced my decision to aim for medicine as a career. I was 16 and dating his eldest daughter, my future wife. My mother-in-law had been to the hospital with "woman's troubles". Bill informed me that she had consulted a 'Vaginacologist' who had sorted it all out! At 16, I thought this sounded like an excellent way to earn a living!

Much to my surprise, my school, Hove Grammar School for Boys, wasn't particularly impressed by my offer of a place at Charing Cross Hospital Medical School. They had only produced one Doctor of Medicine in the previous eight years, so I was expecting pats on the back from all the staff. Before my "transition to academia" most of my energies had been directed to representing the school in various sports. I mistakenly thought the school would be extremely grateful for my efforts. My studies in physics, chemistry and biology hadn't really featured until right at the end of my final term when I started to panic, even though I was only required to attain the lowest pass grades in all three subjects for my acceptance. I proudly announced my offer to my form master who was lost for words and simply passed on the "good news" to the headmaster. After 30 minutes of being dressed down by the Head, I left his office somewhat disillusioned. What really stung was, and I quote "There are scores of students here who are much more deserving of a place at medical school than you." I didn't have an answer to that; well, I did actually but wasn't going to rock the boat any further. I had visions of the horrible man ringing the Dean of "The Cross" telling him to rescind my place, as I was unsuitable.

Ten years later, after I had qualified and become a GP, back in my hometown of Brighton, I received an invitation to give an inspirational lecture to the Sixth Form regarding a career in medicine. Did I take up this invitation? Did I hell.

In the 60s and 70s, medical school teaching was roughly split into the first two years, the pre-clinical years, and the next three years, the Clinical Years. In the pre-clinical period, we studied anatomy, physiology, biochemistry, and pharmacology. This was purely academic, and we didn't see any live patients: only dead ones, or bits of them. This culminated in an examination called 2nd MB that we only had two chances at. If you failed the second time, you were out of medical school. The 1st MB was largely an historical exam, previously taught at medical schools, that was subsequently replaced by "A" levels in physics, chemistry, and biology (or zoology). I found the pre-clinical years pretty tense. The studying was relentless with weekly vivas (oral exams), and end of term exams. To compound my commitment, I opted to take a year out to study for a BSc* in biochemistry!

In the clinical years, we eventually got to see and exam live patients, not all of whom survived the encounter. We were split up into small groups and were attached to various specialties for three to six months at a time. These were called "Firms" and they consisted of General Surgery, General Medicine, Paediatrics, Obstetrics and Gynaecology, Psychiatry, Pathology, among others. At the end of all this, we had to pass our final exams, appropriately titled Final MB. If you failed one or more specialties, you were allowed to retake the exams six months later. We finally gained the qualification of MBBS* and were now proper doctors, or so we thought. After that, we had to complete a pre-registration year in a hospital setting. This consisted of six months as a junior houseman attached to a surgical department, and another six months working in a medical department. We worked extraordinarily long hours as a general dogsbody* to everyone senior to us, which happened to be everyone. After a total of seven years from "A" levels to being "fully-fledged" registered doctors*, we were now qualified to pursue our careers.

We had to either choose General Practice or attempt to climb the slippery pole of a hospital career in the hope of achieving the position of a consultant in one of the various specialties available. If you wanted to become a GP in the community, it became compulsory in the 1970s to join a GP Vocational Training Scheme (VTS). This comprised a rotating six months in various hospital specialties: e.g., Paediatrics, Obstetrics and Gynaecology, Psychiatry, Accident and Emergency, Geriatrics, and Dermatology. It usually started and ended with six months attached to a General Practice as a trainee (now called a registrar). A first-year medical student would be looking at ten years' training to start a career in General Practice. This is complete at the age at which most premier league footballers are coming to the end of their careers, probably with a slightly healthier bank balance but almost certainly with more broken bones and "heading"-induced early onset dementias*. I was a goalkeeper, so I should be OK!

*Vaginacologist: more commonly known as a gynaecologist!

*MBBS Bachelor of Medicine, Bachelor of Surgery.

The use of the name Bachelor for undergraduate degrees probably comes from the old French 'bachelor' meaning apprentice knight and has absolutely nothing to do with my marital status.

*Dogsbody: a person who has to do all the boring or unpleasant jobs that other people do – less commonly dog-robber, which, in the Royal Navy, is a junior officer, or more generally someone who does drudge work. A rough American equivalent would be a "gofer", a grunt, or a lackey. I think I have made my point!

*Registered – with the General Medical Counsel (GMC)

*A study published in October 2019 found that former professional footballers are three and a half times more likely to die of dementia than their peers are. Research at Glasgow University confirmed the link between football and brain damage after investigating claims that heading the ball could cause brain injuries.

Dr D – THE BELMONT MOLE

Much against my mother's wishes I was sent off to the Prep School* my uncle and father had attended in North London, 150 miles away, when I was just over eight years old. My father adored his wife but felt obliged to continue a family tradition and left me at my new school with a whispered request for me to avoid any mention of unhappiness when I wrote home.

The headmaster, who was a friend of my father, and the matron became alarmed that this small boy seemed to cope with school activities but made no friends. I was paired with other boys who were probably displaying the same signs of trauma and taken on trips to zoos, parks, and cinemas with them. This was a ploy that failed dismally. No one was unkind to me, and I wasn't unwell; I suspect I simply entered an emotionally frozen state.

Nevertheless, life went on and I gradually defrosted and began to make a series of friendships, four of which involved men I still regularly see 70 years later, and I cherish our relationships.

There were many unexpected parallels in the lives of Rod and me, one of which is that we were both goalkeepers in our school 1st XI football teams.

Rod, who was tall, agile, and athletic, was on the lowest rung of a sporting ladder that led him up to play for a team that won the London Medical Schools' trophy two years in a row. My position in goal came about because I lacked all the requisite skills around ball control, tackling and the speed to be of any use further up the field. I was quite a fearless keeper and spent a lot of time diving on the ball at the feet of charging opposition forwards.

My last appearance for the school was on a February day when the pitch had been frozen solid for a week and the studs on my boots clattered as I jumped about in an attempt to keep warm. Our team depended for success on the presence of a boy called Bradley, who was also only 12 but looked about 16. Our only tactic was to keep supplying Bradley with the ball so that he could barge his way through the opposition and, occasionally, score.

So, bored, and cold, I was amazed to see a mole wandering across the pitch in front of me presumably unable to get back underground. I had never seen a mole before, nor since, so I carefully picked it up and was stroking its beautiful silky coat when the ball shot past my head. I jumped, the mole bit me, I dropped the mole, and I was sacked.

Many years later, while working at Roedean School, I was offered the opportunity, as a staff member, for my two daughters to attend the school with very low fees. My wife had also had boarding school experience in an attempt to minimize the disruption to her education caused by her father being frequently moved around the country by the Royal Navy. The school accepted no day pupils in those days, so we expressed our gratitude for the offer but chose to keep our two bright and beautiful girls at home.

*Prep school – usually entered at age 8 is the equivalent of a primary school where children in the private sector are tutored before taking the Common Entrance Exam which leads to admission to a Public School.

Dr R – THE PRE-CLINICAL YEARS

My first day at Charing Cross Hospital Medical School was Monday 9 September 1967. I had arrived at my digs in South London the day before. My future wife was already at teacher training college and had spent her first year living at a vicarage between Camberwell Green and the Elephant and Castle. I took over her room, as she was moving out to share with girlfriends. The arrangement was bed and breakfast only, in a very chilly house, shared with a distant vicar and his austere wife of few words. I was extremely lonely as I stayed most evenings and weekends in my room trying to study.

Camberwell Green, down the road, was a great disappointment to me. It sounded as though it would be like Hyde Park, but it turned out to be an extremely busy rectangular roundabout, which would perhaps be more appropriately described as a "rectangularabout" or an "oblongabout" to the older reader. The Elephant and Castle, up the road, provided neither a castle nor elephants roaming about its ramparts. It was just another huge roundabout. At least Camberwell Green had some grass in the centre although mostly inhabited by jolly and often noisy drunks and young people buying and selling small packets of various powders and pills.

After my flattering encounter with the Vice-Dean, I went to

an induction talk in one of the lecture theatres. I sat next to a young man called Dud, who would become my friend, and asked him what he was going to do when he qualified (stupid question really!) He said emphatically that he wanted to be a surgeon and blow me if he didn't end up as a Professor of Breast Surgery at the New Charing Cross Hospital in Fulham and, more importantly, an indispensable member of the highly successful CXHMS (Charing Cross Hospital Medical School) Cup winning Football Team. I simply said I wanted to do a BSc* in Biochemistry so that I could compete with the graduates from Oxford and Cambridge. This I eventually did; it turned out to be a sound decision, as it indirectly helped me enormously in my career.

On the second day, we were introduced to a needle and syringe and given a demonstration on how to take blood. We were then all given a needle and syringe and told to take blood from the student to the immediate left of us. This meant that some inexperienced novice was going to jab something nasty into my arm. Amazingly, all went well, and 45 samples of fresh blood were sent off to the laboratory for analysis without anyone's consent, as far as I can remember. Mine came back normal but we did learn later that some poor girl in the year above me had found out that she was suffering from early asymptomatic leukaemia. She married one of the lads in the football squad but subsequently died in her last year before qualifying. To this day, I regret not visiting her in the last few days of her life in hospital.

On the third day, I was introduced to the donated body that I was going to dissect, bit by bit, over the next year and a half.

My new best friend, the budding surgeon, and I were to study one side of the corpse with two other freshers on the other side. Every week we were examined by the anatomy demonstrator on our progress and had to pass before proceeding onto the next stage. I found these relentless examinations pretty stressful. However, I was not as stressed as the poor female student in the previous year had been; she had fainted in the dissection room when she thought she recognised her grandmother on the table. I'm not sure how truthful this story was, but I guess it was bound to happen eventually. It wouldn't have bothered me unduly, as I didn't particularly like my grandparents!

On the fourth day, I bought, at great expense, my very own skeleton together with its own genuine wooden coffin for convenient carriage on London Transport. Often the trains were very crowded. I remember sitting on a seat with my box on my lap. Occasionally I would lift the lid far enough to allow a bony hand to be seen poking out. This always had the desired effect of my fellow passengers giving me just a little more room on my journeys. I nicknamed my new friend Slim.

A few months later, Dud and I gave up an afternoon to dissect the complete gastrointestinal* tract. We had the anatomy room to ourselves and in a matter of minutes had all the guts from oesophagus to anus stretched out across the laboratory floor, some 30 feet long. Dud had beautifully cut out the lower intestines while I concentrated on the upper bits. In order to clear out the contents of this long pipe I connected the upper part to a tap while Dud held the lower bits over a sink. The tap was turned on full. It was pretty obvious that I was more suited to biochemistry as my efforts at surgery resulted in multiple fountains of 'shitty water' spraying the walls and floor of the anatomy room. In my haste, I had nicked the walls of the bowel with my scalpel blade. It was not a good time for the head of department to put in an appearance.

I was elected the secretary to the football team. This was a huge honour for me until I realised that my only role was to collect all the filthy kit after a match and present it back at the next game. I was expected to fund this myself and was very short of cash, so I found myself washing all eleven shirts, shorts, and socks in the bath at the vicarage. Then I would lug the soaking and partially cleaned clothing to the local launderette to dry, while I enjoyed my fish and chip supper next door at the chippy, plus or minus mushy peas (when I could afford it). However, the football team saved me from my misery at the vicarage as a room had become available at a large house in Blackheath, where two of my football chums were already living. Three of us shared two bedrooms in a family home comprising a married couple, their two children and a dog. I was fortunate to have a room to myself while the other two shared. The surrounding area was great, and we all enjoyed full board, which was an absolute luxury, although the weekly meatloaf became a bit challenging. We were all there for a year until we finished our pre-clinical studies and went our separate ways, having passed our exams, which led us on to our clinical studies, i.e., actually seeing patients. I was extremely fortunate to marry my teacher girlfriend at this stage of my studies, and we moved to a lovely, unfurnished one-bedroom flat in Highgate,

North London. I took a year out of medicine to study for a BSc in biochemistry. This process confirmed to me that I didn't want to be a scientist but preferred to see and treat patients directly. The extra qualification, without doubt, made applying for jobs much less difficult when I eventually qualified. We had three happy years there, with my wife teaching in Hackney and me studying at Charing Cross.

*The gastrointestinal tract is the tract from the mouth to the anus (more commonly known to the layman as the "arsehole"!)

Dr D – FRESHERS DAY

I left home to become a medical student in September 1962. After working for a month as a labourer for John Laing on the site of the new M6 motorway service station at Keele, I had repaid a debt to my father and fattened up my Post Office Savings account.

Very few of the London medical schools had any student accommodation so I had applied for the cheapest option, which was to share a room in "digs" listed by the University of London Lodgings Bureau.

Dragging most of my worldly possessions in a bulging suitcase, I made my way to a large house, close to The Standard pub in Blackheath. It was owned by an elderly Hungarian doctor, whose much younger wife coped with him, their two young daughters and six Guy's students.

She was a sweet, energetic woman who did all the housework, looked after us all very well and fed us like kings.

I was fortunate to have been allocated a roommate, David, with whom I became firm friends – we are still in touch. We occupied a large, unheated, draughty attic room through one of the coldest winters on record and survived by spending most of the time between meals studying, fully clothed, in bed. Glasses of water froze during the night.

The first day of the Freshers' Day agenda at the medical school included a "you're lucky to be here" address from a diminutive professor, after a formal speech of greeting by the Dean. We were then split into groups and shown round the building. This included a visit to the Anatomy Theatre, which hosted about a dozen cadavers on white china slabs, covered in green plastic sheeting. It was reputed to be an event that caused one or two students every year to reassess their decision to study medicine.

The last event of the day was a gathering of the 90 or so of us at a reception where we were encouraged to join sports clubs and organisations like The Christian Union. There were about 10 brown-faced fellow students, and our intake included a good proportion of female students.

I'm not very clubbable even now, but back then, after 10 years of single-sex schooling, compulsory sport, the CCF (combined cadet force) and daily chapel services, twice on Sundays, I had no hesitation in rejecting all their blandishments.

My aim was to explore London with the help of beautiful and compliant women.

The dress code of the male students was very revealing. The public-school boys, especially those from outside London, tended to look like the dummies on view in the windows of the gentlemen's outfitters found in the High Streets of county towns. This involved tweed jackets, viyella shirts, woollen or club ties and occasionally cavalry twill trousers in contrast to the grammar schoolboys in blazers and grey flannel trousers. All the women wore blouses, skirts, sensible shoes and not much make-up, if my memory serves me well.

This was where I began another good and long-lasting friendship.

"And who are you?" The "and" made the question sound slightly patronising.

"My name is Duncan Stewart, and you are Neil Watson," I replied reading the name from the name tape sewn on the short end of his rather dilapidated school tie.

Then we exchanged family details in order to establish exactly which micro layer of the middle class we belonged to.

His father was a colonel in the RAMC (Royal Army Medical Corp), while mine was the editor of a research publication, who also ran a society for the benefit of the scientists and industrialists involved in the ceramic industry. His mother was a fine artist, mine a very competent secretary, but neither of them worked. I had a younger brother and he had two younger sisters.

One fragment of our rather forensic discussion, which I managed to embarrass him with by resurrecting it for many years, requires you to know that at that time I was skinny, six foot tall, red-haired, freckled and blue eyed.

"My mother was born in Chile," I said in an attempt to make my family history sound a bit more exotic. Her grandparents had been economic migrants from Edinburgh in the 1860's.

"So, your father must be white."

Neil had completed his "A" levels at 16 and spent a year amusing himself drawing architectural landscapes in Florence, rowing, practicing the violin and repairing an old car, all pursuits at which he was irritatingly competent.

It may have been true that one of our number, when the green plastic bag was lifted from "their" cadaver, on our first Monday morning anatomy session, found herself staring at the naked corpse of her old headmistress. Around table six, I was delighted to find myself in the company of two of the best-looking women and three other lads, two from South Wales and one from Cornwall, along with the preserved mortal remains of quite a short old man.

We spent many months dissecting our cadaver with little skill and, to be honest, diminishing enthusiasm. However, we did learn some anatomy. We were tested once a month on our findings by one of the Anatomy Demonstrators, who were all training to become surgeons.

"Does anyone know what is unusual about the facial muscles you have been identifying?"

"Yes," said Diana, one of my fellow students. She seemed keen to impress our good-looking persecutor. "The muscles of expression are not attached bone to bone but from skin to skin"

"Very good," he responded, beaming, "and are any of you aware of a similar situation anywhere else in the body?"

There was a moment's silence.

"Oh, yes," gushed Diana now firmly established as the only competent anatomist among us, "the Dartos muscles of the scrotum," she added triumphantly.

After a slight pause, he replied in a sombre tone, "That knowledge, my dear, is the sign of a misspent youth," and walked away leaving four smirking males and the brightest blush I have ever witnessed.

Dr R – ODD JOBS

After passing 2nd MB, I went on to study for a BSc in Biochemistry, which took another four terms. During this time, I married Heather, and went to live in a rather lovely ground floor flat in Highgate, North London. Despite going to a family planning clinic and being instructed in the use of the then fashionable Dutch Cap*, Heather soon became pregnant. I was delighted, although I was slighted bemused to find the contraceptive still in its wrapping under the bed a few weeks later! My grant and Heather's earnings never seemed to be enough, so I was always on the lookout for ways to fund the rest of my training. Most universities in the UK operate a system of three terms a year, each lasting about 10 weeks. That is 30 weeks out of a total of 52. We also went into the rotation of "firms", e.g., Medicine, Surgery, Paediatrics, Psychiatry, Obstetrics, and Gynaecology etc., each lasting 12 or 24 weeks, 48 weeks out of 52. The bottom line was that we studied with four weeks holiday a year squashed between firms. This didn't leave much room for manoeuvre, but it wasn't impossible. One evening a week I cleaned out the offices of my father-in-law's factory in the East End, off the Mile End Road. Every Christmas, I helped deliver the post in North London. I was given the same round each year. I never delivered post to a block of flats that had a lift, and that bag was blooming heavy! Babysitting was the easiest option, as I spent evenings studying in lovely houses and flats in wealthy Highgate; being paid for it was a bonus. I had regular clients including Michael Mansfield, the famous barrister, and several film directors, albeit minor ones. I also met Simon Rattle, then a 16-year-old lodger studying at The Royal College of Music, before he went on be one of the UK's most famous conductors. I kept in touch with one or two of my clients, but sadly many have now passed away.

My father-in-law changed factories on one occasion only to find he found 50 brand new children's school desks in a lock-up. He had no use for them, so I took them off his hands. As it was coming up for Christmas, I was able to sell them, going from door to door, and also piggybacking onto the ends of markets, mostly at the Angel Islington. I had no overheads so was able to offer them at a bargain price.

London was always plunging into darkness in the winter due to power cuts lasting hours at a time. I had the idea of making and selling candles. I read up about it and acquired clear wax blocks, and wicks and dyes from a candle-making outlet off the Fulham Road. The new Charing Cross Hospital was then being built in Fulham, and I was able to find discarded plastic pipes in various diameters, which provided the basics of my standard candle.

I made a bit of a mess of our cooker back at the flat, melting down mountains of wax into my homemade moulds. I used to pray for power-cuts; when they occurred, I would rush down to the main Highgate tube station exit and have a lucrative evening's business. Standing there in the gloom, holding a lighted candle in my hand, was the perfect setting for success. At great expense, I was able to purchase the rubber mould that would provide the basis of a ten-inch penis-shaped working candle that was supported by the shape of two ample testicles. I sold these as limited-edition items. They came in three colours: red, black, and natural. One consultant surgeon bought all three, so I was able to offer him a reasonable discount!

My most successful source of income was my ladies' tights empire. I used to convert my student grant every term into 1,000 pairs of tights (trade name "Fantasy"). They came in one shade only, with very attractive packaging. I sold these for five shillings each (in old money – 25p today) or five pairs for one pound. It was quite a bargain. My customers were mostly nurses, domestic workers, and the occasional consultant's mistress. Another popular outlet came while doing my stint in the old VD clinic, where I was popular with some of the sex workers I was treating. One of the girls offered to pay me in kind! I wasn't sure how successful the treatment for gonorrhoea and syphilis was at the time, so I declined gracefully. A good decision, I think. I was often spotted walking the hospital wards and various outpatient departments with a bulging briefcase. This was assumed to be full of various medical books and I acquired a reputation for being rather keen among the teaching staff. However, this all changed when my case burst open in the middle of a busy "Gender Identification Clinic", dispersing numerous pairs of "Fantasy" tights at the feet of the psychiatric consultant!

The degree course in biochemistry took us to The London

Hospital in the East End, a stone's throw (or was it a knife!) from the Kray Twins'* old stomping ground, and to The Chelsea College in well – er – Chelsea! Mostly, we were based at our medical school biochemistry labs. I enjoyed the academic side of these studies but was never quite sure what was going on during the practical laboratory work. During one particular experiment at The Chelsea College, out of exasperation, I pushed an innocuous button on the wall only to be greeted three minutes later by the sirens of two fire engines. I was never sure if the firemen were annoyed at the false alarm or relieved that the laboratory (full of very flammable liquids) was not about to explode. Fortunately for me, the source of the disturbance was never ascertained as I wasn't going to own up – I had my career to think of.

As medical students, my friend John and I took part in some overnight neurophysiology research requiring us to sleep over at the West London Hospital with EEG* leads stuck to our scalps. Initially, we could not sleep, so we decided to walk into the A&E department at 2am in the morning mimicking catatonia* with our unusual headgear. This threw the department into chaos! While the staff were trying to sort out where we had come from, we disappeared back to our beds. We never knew nor asked what happened next.

England won the World Cup in 1966 on home soil, beating West Germany 4-2. Four years later Alf Ramsey, who was now Sir Alf Ramsey was still in charge of the national team. The competition was to be played at high altitude in Mexico. The medical school was approached to take part in some research on the effects this would have on our footballers. I cannot remember the actual details of the research project, I think it was something to do with salt supplements, but I do remember being part of it because we had to collect all our urine over two weeks. This was extremely difficult to negotiate while working on the wards and going to lectures. On three occasions, we had to present our backsides so that some heavy-handed nurse could insert a small electrode up our anus to measure something or other (electrical potential seems to ring a bell!) On the first two occasions, my anus went into spasm and broke the unwelcome probe. I was informed, in a rather unsympathetic manner, that they were very expensive. By the third time I got the hang of relaxing, probably because they threatened not to pay me if I broke any more of their kit! I certainly earned that small fee, but to this day, I cherish the personal letter of thanks from Sir Alf himself, despite England not being so successful that time. We, the volunteers, were also treated to an England International at Wembley Stadium, which was my first visit. I didn't have the opportunity to mention to Sir Alf that I had played for Sussex School Boys in goal and that I was disappointed not to have been spotted at least for an England trial. In fact, I don't think any of us actually met the man.

Charing Cross Hospital was the smallest medical school in London, but we had the proudest football team. On our way to the London Medical Schools Football cup final, we had to overcome a team whose football facilities were in some awful places off the North Circular Road in London. We had fantastic premises down at Cobham, so fantastic that Chelsea Football Club has since bought up the whole area. Three of our team almost didn't make it; the Mini they were in was involved in a road traffic accident on the way to the game. No one was obviously injured. However, one of the passengers (we will call him Alan) was my left back. I was in goal as usual and we were up against a strong opposition. I needed all the support I could muster. Alan wasn't having his best match, not helped by receiving an injury early in the game. Somehow, he ran into the centre forward's elbow. I spent most of my game shouting at him and covering up for his incompetence. Much to my annoyance, he spent halftime in the dressing room having a kip while the rest of us were discussing tactics. We went on to win, only just, no thanks to our sleepy defender. It was one of those "games of two halves". In the last 10 minutes, our inside right "nutmegged" the opposition centre half, "found the target", "pulled the trigger" and scored. Then we successfully "parked the bus" until the glorious end, a 1 – 0 victory. Alan's lack of concentration was soon forgotten during our post-match meal at the opposition's clubhouse. He didn't feel great on the way home in the battered Mini so was dropped off at the Accident and Emergency department of the old Charing Cross Hospital, off The Strand in London. The President of our football team, a Mr Arthur Makey, kindly popped in and removed Alan's shattered kidney that very evening!

I had not met Mr Arthur Makey before he arrived in our changing room at Cobham when we were preparing for the inter-London Hospital Medical Schools cup final. I was in goal, but unfortunately, five days earlier I had stuffed my left middle finger into an ice-crushing machine. I was studying for my BSc at the time and didn't really understand what was going on in the laboratory so the two other students on the course would vote for me to go in early to sort out the ice required for the day's experiments. The ice was produced in cubes from the freezer, but we needed it crushed. However, the ancient machine got blocked and, without turning the machine off, I successfully repaired it with my frozen left middle finger. I did feel a slight tug, but it was only when I was rinsing my hands under hot water that feelings returned. I noticed two one-inch gashes on my terminal phalanx*. The A&E department was just down the road, so I popped in before I bled to death! I didn't receive much sympathy from the casualty officer who treated me like some sort of idiot. Eight painful stitches later (I have a feeling he forgot to inject a local anaesthetic before the operation), I was back in the laboratory. News got through to the football captain, who rang me that evening; he treated me as if I was an idiot as well. Five days later, I was interviewed in the changing room toilets by the great Mr Arthur Makey. To cut a long story a little shorter he offered (no, he didn't actually offer) to perform an anaesthetic ring block at the base of my injured digit. This was blooming painful but if it helped the team with a better performing goalkeeper then that was alright by me. It was another game of "two halves" for me as I was escorted back into the toilet at halftime for a back-up injection. I was beginning to worry whether the feelings would ever return to my poor old finger. We won the cup and my place at medical school was vindicated. I thought I was a bit of a hero at the time, but I don't think this feeling was shared by the rest of the team. Mr Makey, however, remembered my dedication and when I qualified several years later, I applied to be his House Surgeon. I got the job. How could he refuse?

*Dutch Cap: the contraceptive diaphragm or cap is a circular dome of thin, soft silicone that is inserted into the vagina before sex – this can take up to 30 minutes and so for many men proved to be a very successful contraceptive! It was thought at the time that the Dutch were having a bit of a laugh at the UK's expense.

*The Kray twins were the foremost perpetrators of organised crime in the East End of London from the late 1950s to 1967. They often amused themselves with a bit of amateur surgery themselves.

*The terminal phalanx is the last bit of a finger

*EEG: an electro encephalogram is a recording of brain activity. Small sensors are attached to the scalp to pick up the electrical signals produced when brain cells send messages to each other. John couldn't sleep and spent most of the night reading a copious supply of Playboy Magazines. I did wonder if this might have sabotaged the results somewhat!

*Catatonia is a neuropsychiatric behaviour syndrome that is characterised by abnormal movements, immobility, abnormal behaviours, and withdrawal

Dr D – EXAM TECHNIQUE

Passing the 2nd MB exam, the gateway to becoming a clinical student, was a high hurdle even though the written exams were set by those who taught us. It was the vivas that I found a real challenge. As a teenage blusher and stammerer, I dreaded the public exposure in a scenario where ignorance could create such potential embarrassment, as opposed to the written exams, where your stupidity was only shared with your examiner.

My mother had surgery for breast cancer a few weeks before the onset of exam hostilities and I was given compassionate leave to go home to Stoke to see her and support my father, who was devastated by the fear of losing his wife and not coping well, having no domestic skills of any kind.

I got back to London in time to sit the written exam and felt I had done just about well enough. Next came the dreaded oral (viva voce) exams. I have no memory of any of them except the anatomy session for which we were expected to have become familiar with all the major structures in the human body (of which there are a frighteningly large number, many unknown to this frightened examinee).

My surname put me close to the end of our year group in the alphabetical order. By the time my turn came, the inquisitors were getting a bit bored. They were not yet in sight of the end and a pint in The Grapes and were, occasionally, a little bit mischievous.

The Gordon Museum, then housed at Guy's, opened in 1905. It contained many historically significant preserved anatomical specimens and many models of "the interior structure of the human body", fashioned in wax by Joseph Townes, a man to whom I had not expected to feel any gratitude. A selection of these exhibits had been wheeled out by our examiners.

I was confronted by a life-sized wax model of the anatomy of the thigh, complete with nerves and blood vessels, all in vivid colours against a background of pink muscle and white bone.

"What is this structure?" asked my examiner, one of the demonstrators from the Dept of Anatomy, pointing to the bright red representation of the femoral artery. There was a resigned tone to his voice that prompted me to an entirely irrational act of absurd bravado

"I think that may be the Central Line, sir," I offered with a straight face.

"Right, so this would be...?" now pointing to the navy-blue Femoral Vein

"Almost certainly the Piccadilly Line, sir"

"So, this point of intersection would be at Oxford Circus?"

"No sir, I think you will find this occurs at Holborn Station, sir"

All this was conducted in mock serious tones. Then my examiner wandered off and came back with the Professor of Anatomy, a benign old chap with a full head of white hair and a pipe permanently clenched between his teeth.

"Dr Stewart here thinks that the London Underground system

was designed in accordance with the vascular anatomy of the lower limb. Professor, do you think that is plausible?"

The two of them continued this idiotic conversation while I joyfully counted down the remaining seconds of what was usually a 10-minute session. One last question about lymphatic drainage, and then it was me who was in The Grapes!

Three years later, most of us were taking two sets of final exams; those set by the Royal Colleges, known as The Conjoint, which qualified you to continue a medical career, and those which conferred a University of London degree, if you passed them. It was a hugely stressful period with exams spread over three months, held away from the familiar territory of Guy's.

You probably don't give much thought to the colour of your urine. However, having been taught about various drugs and diseases that discoloured it, I had at some point wasted some time working out how an almost complete spectrum might occur. There was Blackwater fever; the red staining of bloody urine; the dark yellow of jaundice; the brighter shade of yellow conferred by a urinary antiseptic drug; the pinkish colour that appeared after taking some aperient mixtures or eating beetroot; and the occasional appearance of a stain called Methylene Blue which was concentrated by the kidneys and used to prove that what was thought to be urine was urine.

This apparently pointless discursion saved me from ignominy at a medical viva, during which my examiner had been very considerate by glossing over a couple of questions I had answered inadequately.

"Do you know anything about what gives urine its characteristic smell?"

"No sir, I'm afraid I don't, but I am an expert on the discolouration of urine." I then managed to waffle on about how a combination of extremely unlikely coincidences could produce a positive rainbow of colours until the bell rang and my ordeal was over.

One of my fellow students doing the Conjoint Obstetrics and Gynaecology viva found himself in front of a large woman with short grey hair, half glasses and a very loud voice. She was the professor at a rival medical school and known to have a very low tolerance of student ignorance in her area of expertise

"Describe the anatomy of the vagina."

My friend got the structure and coordinates just about right but then made the fatal mistake of describing the direction of this fine muscular tube as being inwards and upwards.

"No," boomed his nemesis. "Downwards and outwards." He was failed and had to re-sit the entire exam.

Dr R – NOT AS CLEVER AS I THOUGHT

I clearly remember the first night a mate of mine and I were released onto the wards at the New Charing Cross Hospital in West London. I think the general idea was to gain experience on how the hospital ran out of hours, principally from the Accident and Emergency department to admissions on the General Medical and Surgical wards. Paediatrics was to come later in our training. Casualty had calmed down by midnight so, with stethoscopes dangling around our necks and sporting brand new long white coats we cruised into one of the medical wards demanding tea and chocolate biscuits from one of the junior nurses on duty for the night, who was clearly in awe of us. She scampered off to the kitchens while we put our tired feet up on the sister's desk in her office, as you do, enjoying our newly found status. Not only a pot of tea and biscuits, but also a plate of freshly made cheese sandwiches duly arrived.

After half an hour of discussing our future brilliant careers, we sauntered off to our rooms for a bit of a kip; we had an early start on the wards in the morning. However, we didn't get much sleep as we were up all night on the loo peeing for England. I can only surmise that a diuretic must have accidently slipped into the pot of tea. Unfortunately, that particularly helpful nurse had been working for an agency, and we never saw her again. A few weeks later and fully rehydrated I found myself assisting at an above-the-knee amputation of a man's right leg. This poor chap was only in his sixties but had been an insulin dependent diabetic most of his life and had developed gangrene because of his compromised circulation.

Maggots had invaded the afflicted limb, which is not uncommon in this situation and actually no bad thing, as these little friends kept the wound clean and free from infection. My extremely important role in all this was, for two long hours, to hold the leg steady while the surgeon slowly dissected away. This surgeon was at least a foot shorter than me, so the operating table was set at a height about the level of my knees. My back, consequently, was killing me but it didn't stop me being a bit of a smart-arse*. When the leg was finally removed from its owner, I duly passed it to over to the junior surgical nurse standing next to me. I explained to her that as part of the professor's ongoing research she would need to remove all the maggots, make an accurate count and report back as soon as possible. "Yes sir," she gulped (I liked that), and off she went.

Two minutes later there was a slight tug on the back of my trouser waistband, and I felt the contents of a tube of very cold KY jelly* slowly run down my bottom cleavage*. It was hot in the operating theatre and, I have to admit, the sensation was initially not at all unpleasant. A little later however, when the jelly had warmed up, it became extremely sticky and unwelcome. I was scrubbed up and had to endure this torture for nearly another hour before I could change my underwear. It was not as if I carried spare underpants around with me!

Although all the nursing staff wore surgical masks, their eyes gave away their knowing smirks. Getting one over on nurses as cocky medical students wasn't going to be as easy as I had initially thought. I guess they had seen it all before.

---

*If you don't know what "smart-arse" means, perhaps you shouldn't be reading a low-powered self-indulgence like this!

*If you do know the meaning of "bottom-cleavage", you definitely shouldn't be reading a high-powered medical tome like this!

*KY Jelly is a water-based, water-soluble personal lubricant, most commonly used as a lubricant for sexual intercourse or masturbation. I think the implication was that the nursing staff thought I was a bit of a "wanker" and needed some help!

Dr D – EMPTY POCKETS

My parents were generous people, but both came from Scottish families for whom honesty, hard work and thriftiness were more important attributes than anything else. Therefore, if you needed spending money you had to earn it. In school holidays I worked as a bread delivery boy, did the Royal Mail delivery at Christmas, painted our house with a masonry paint called Snowcem, twice blocking the main drain, and worked in the Diamond Clay Company that fired huge slabs of fire clay, destined to line furnaces, in an ancient bottle kiln. Finally, just before leaving for medical school, I spent those three weeks working as a chippy's mate at the Keele service station.

There weren't many ways of earning money in London as a pre-clinical student, partly because, until we moved on to be clinical students, we were only available during the term times.

My income was £8 a week, provided equally by my father and the Stoke-on-Trent Education Department. This was expected to cover all expenses – rent, travel, lunches, and books – and, in fairness, it did so, with small supplements from relatives and my savings.

One of my fellow students, a few years older than the rest of us, had already qualified as a pharmacist in South Africa and now supplemented his income by working in the pharmacies of a small, very well positioned chain of central London chemists. He got me a job serving behind the counter at one of these shops, on the corner of Oxford Street and Edgware Road, right opposite Hyde Park. I worked a 1pm – 8pm session on Saturday nights and 10am – 1pm on a Sunday, if I was needed. We were paid in cash as we left. It was a very busy place.

One of my fellow shop assistants was an anxious 17-year-old girl called Anna, who worked there full-time. She often got a bit flustered but was much liked by the customers. She was a huge pop fan and had an encyclopaedic knowledge of the current state of the charts and the group gossip. Nothing had prepared her for the thrill of having to serve the drummer in The Hollies. I had never really believed that such moments could result in incontinence – but this one did.

We had a lot of Arab customers who frequently requested "a blood cleaner and laxative". I must have sold thousands of senna tablets and bottles of strangely coloured aperient liquids. The other frequently requested items were condoms. Predictably, the male customers gravitated to the male assistant, with the transaction discussed in whispered conversation. However, there were exceptions, and especially on Saturday evenings, when the girls on the game in the park were regulars. I had made the mistake on one occasion of truthfully answering the question of what my name was from one woman, who wore a large fur coat regardless of the weather. Big mistake.

"You got a girlfriend Duncan?" she said in a very loud voice.

"Yes, I have thanks; how many of these do you want?"

"You seein' 'er tonight are yer Duncan?"

"No actually I'm not." Another mistake. She loosened the belt on her coat just enough to prove that that was all she was wearing.

"Well, I'm free darling; business is never good when it's cold like now, so what time do yer get off?" Laughter all round.

I seem to remember leaving by the back door.

Dr R – THREE OPERATIONS

Three operations come to mind that I found upsetting if not a little painful as a medical student. The first was assisting a breast surgeon. A very pretty art college student, in her wisdom, had decided that her breasts were too small. At great expense, she had had implants a few months before. I saw photos of the before and after breast enlargement, and the before looked OK to me, but that's not really relevant, is it? Anyway, these wretched implants had ruptured, leaving her breasts deflated and very knobbly. The surgeon cleared out the mess as best as he could and put her back together again. I went to see her post-op in the ward, and she was extremely distressed about the outcome. I'm sure that some sort of reconstruction would have improved things, but the results were never going to be as good as her original breasts, although that's only my opinion.

The second operation was technically very simple, but the story was horrific. A very disturbed young pianist had failed some musical exams and consequently became depressed to the point that he had tried to kill himself. He had attempted this by trying to electrocute himself, the details of which I cannot recall. The results, however, I remember very well. The ends of all his fingers and thumbs were seriously burnt and destroyed. Watching the surgeon scrape off all this dead tissue together with the offensive odour of burnt flesh hanging in the air was very challenging. I guess we can all relate to having our fingers burnt, but you had to multiply this experience by 100 – and what happened to his promising career?

The third operation was very rare in the UK back in the early seventies. It involved the removal of a man's genitalia and the construction of a false vagina. I spent time with the man pre-op in the ward and, a day later, with the woman, post-op. The operation was a success and I only hope her new life was too. I didn't discuss the actual operation with her because, from what I saw, I didn't think at the time that would have been a great idea. When the patient was under a general anaesthetic, he was injected with some medication that caused him to have an erection. The surgeon then neatly cut four incisions from glans to scrotum and peeled back the skin like a banana. There were four of us, all first-year clinical medical students, and every one of us was holding onto our crotch for dear life! I feel so fortunate that, to date, I don't appear to have any gender identification issues. But I guess there is still time!

Dr D – GUY'S CONSULTANTS

At the end of every three-month period of specialist clinical attachments, known as "firms", it was customary for one of the students to arrange a dinner to which we invited our consultant, and we would pay for it. They were usually very enjoyable and relaxed events at which the senior staff let their hair down, a bit. It was my turn to make the arrangements at the end of the Psychiatry firm. My problem was that the proposed date fell just before we received our grants, and everyone was skint, so it had to be a budget event. I consulted a friend I had made in my local launderette, who was an expert on pubs in The City, and he did a deal for us at a pub in Bishopsgate. We could have a steak dinner in an upstairs room plus soup and trifle for about 10 shillings. (In today's money just over £12!)

The dinner would have been an unqualified success if our very popular consultant DS-C (David Stafford-Clark) had not been reading poetry on the BBC Third programme and arrived very late. By the time he did arrive, we had all been drinking for far too long with no food. Now we could all eat; our guest was served a freshly cooked steak and we had plates of food that had been kept warm for over an hour. The publican finally ejected us at about 11pm and I staggered off towards my flat in Highbury. Five minutes later, a car drew up beside me and the senior registrar told me that his boss had really enjoyed the evening and we were all invited to his house in Dulwich for another drink. My first mistake was getting into the car. The second was asking for something "long" and accepting the very large gin and tonic produced by our benevolent host.

I was the last to arrive. I was seated at the end of a very long white leather sofa in his beautiful modern sitting room with fine views over South London. I finished my drink and quietly slid unconscious onto the parquet floor where I was later told I had spent some time before anyone noticed my absence. I was also told that they had loaded me into a car at some point, but then pulled me out and left me on the driveway, because no one knew where I lived.

At 4am in the morning, I woke up on a camp bed in a garage, next to a sleek Jaguar saloon. The naked bulb hanging over my head illuminated a large piece of paper with the message "You are quite safe. Take these." with an arrow pointing to the four soluble Aspirin tablets laid out in a perfect square.

I did as I was told and was woken by 7am by my involuntary host bringing me a mug of tea, a toothbrush and razor and then escorting me to his bathroom. A little later, we set off for Guy's, where he parked in his designated space behind The York Clinic, accepted my effusive apologies and reassured me that the events of the previous night would not affect my medical career unfavourably.

I didn't see him again during the following two years before I graduated. However, 20 years later, while I was seated at my desk completing a BUPA claim form, my secretary came into my consulting room carrying a small beige medical card. She said it belonged to a man in the waiting room who would like to become a patient as he had established that I was a Guy's graduate.

The waiting room was empty, except for the good doctor, whose immediate response on seeing me was "Oh my God, it's you!"

He didn't accept my offer to return his card, and I had the pleasure of looking after him until he died in 1999.

Dr Walter Banville, Physician to Her Majesty and the Royal Household, was one of the many eminent and justly admired consultants in whose wake I trailed during numerous largely unmemorable ward rounds but one of his involved an event that I have always remembered.

The august doctor had clearly decided before the round began that he was going to demonstrate to us raw recruits the finer points of one part of a comprehensive physical examination, and the very shapely young ward sister, a relatively recent appointment, had made the appropriate arrangements.

After about 90 minutes of moving from bed to bed and discussing the problems of each occupant, a conversation in which the patient rarely seemed to participate, we appeared to be reaching the end when we arrived at a bed with its curtains drawn. Sister, wearing a starched white headdress, dark blue uniform with a breast level pocket for scissors and one of those watches that hang upside down, a wide black belt with an ornate silver buckle and black stockings and shoes, drew back the curtains with a flourish.

The unfortunate patient chosen for the demonstration was a sad looking man of about 40 who was lying, uncovered, on his left side, with his pyjama trousers round his ankles, and his naked, probably cold bottom right at the edge of the mattress. Without a word to the patient Dr B explained at great length the importance of our overcoming any reluctance to examine a patient's anus and rectum, and the indications for doing so.

Right on cue, Sister proffered a rubber glove and then opened a fresh tube of lubricant gel.

The great man, still addressing his followers, leaned over the patient, and thrust his digit through the anus. He was about to tell us what he hoped to find, or indeed had found, when what was apparent to his audience became acutely apparent to him.

His fine silk tie had decided to accompany the probing finger and he was now tethered to the arse of a man he barely knew and to whom he had certainly not yet spoken.

"Don't just stand there woman, cut it off."

I think these were his last words before he made as dignified an exit from the ward as possible, for a man with black jacket, striped trousers and an amputated MCC tie.

The patient who had no means of knowing why his bed was surrounded by 15 smirking students continued to sport this unusual anal adornment until a student nurse was instructed to remove it.

The old medical wards in Guy's Hospital appeared to be exactly the same as they did in those black and white photos featuring Florence Nightingale and her colleagues. They were long, high-ceilinged rooms with about 15 beds, three feet apart, on both sides. All patient care was arranged to focus on the weekly consultant ward round. For my first three months as a clinical student this was conducted by Dr Jackson. These weekly events were a cause of high anxiety for everyone, except perhaps Dr J himself. The junior staff needed to perform efficiently and display their erudition in order to attract glowing references when applying for their next posts. We students, who were deemed to be erudition-free, were standing targets for being ridiculed for our ignorance by everyone else.

Newly admitted patients were allocated to a student who was expected to "clerk" them as soon as possible. This meant practicing our skills at eliciting and recording an accurate history of the patients' health, examining them, making a tentative diagnosis, and suggesting appropriate investigations. The houseman then repeated the process and initiated treatment, following which a more senior doctor checked all the details in order to avoid embarrassing mistakes being discovered during the dreaded ward round.

The greatest potential for humiliation came when the group was asked to provide a list of the possible causes of a symptom or physical signs, such as jaundice. The first 10 causes were fairly obvious, but then it became a process like musical chairs, which halted if you could not provide the next possible answer, at which point everyone stared disapprovingly. It was even more embarrassing if you provided an incorrect suggestion.

The main cause of all this angst, Dr J, was a quietly spoken, unsmiling man of about 65. He had well-groomed grey hair, gold-rimmed half-glasses, a stiff white collar above a striped shirt, a dreary tie, black jacket and waistcoat, gold watchchain, striped black trousers and plain black Oxford shoes. Some of the younger consultants wore dark suits, but the old pre-war uniform still predominated at this time.

On one memorable Friday the crocodile of doctors and students, with Dr J and the ward sister at its head, was moving slowly clockwise around the ward stopping at his patients, whose problems were discussed in detail. When we reached the end of the beds on the left side, we came to a closed door I had never seen opened. We all stopped, and a mumbled conversation took place between the senior doctors, before Dr J opened the door and strode in.

Sitting on the bed in this small room was a man of about 40, looking wild eyed and agitated. As soon as he saw our revered leader, he launched an impressive verbal barrage:

"Doctor fucking Jackson, and about fucking time too, I've been in this shitty room for four fucking days and no fucker has been to fucking see me...."

This went on for a couple of minutes, during which time Dr J, who had presumably faced greater problems during the war, stood motionless until the man ran out of expletives.

He then turned to his houseman, who looked a bit confused, and said, "Dr Nawab, I think you should call our esteemed psychiatric colleague, and tell him it's fucking urgent."

These were days when the F word still had the power to shock.

Dr R – STAGE FRIGHT

My first house job was at the New Charing Cross Hospital under a surgical firm. This was in stark contrast to my post in a medical firm, six months later, at the old Brighton General Hospital. It had been a workhouse in a previous life and pretty much felt like it during my six months there. I was one of two house physicians covering a male and female ward. Our on-call duties were, therefore, every other night and every other weekend. Peter, my other half, married one of the nurses soon after the end of our time together. I was his best man, and it was the first time I saw him out of the hospital. The post-graduate centre was in the hospital grounds, and the housemen were expected to give the odd lecture to the local GPs after they had been bribed to come with a hearty lunch, usually supplied by one of the pharmaceutical companies. Although I was comfortable talking to small numbers, I found giving a lecture to approximately 60 doctors extremely daunting. Basically, I got stage fright and would do anything to avoid it. However, I was trapped into sharing a 60-minute slot with Peter. I was due to give the first lecture on psoriasis*, a subject I knew very little about, so I had had to do a lot of mugging up in preparation.

We were presented to the post-prandial sleepy crowd by the Post Graduate Dean, who invited Dr Peter to talk first, which wasn't the order we had agreed. This was a disaster for me as I had taken 10mgs of Valium* in the toilets to steady my nerves. It certainly worked, as I fell asleep during Peter's scintillating lecture on a subject that I can't recall. The Post Graduate Dean had to wake me up for my offering. Needless to say, I was very relaxed, and it went brilliantly, although to be honest, I remember nothing about it!

*Psoriasis is a long lasting, non-contagious autoimmune disease characterised by areas of abnormal skin, which are often red or purple but may also be dry, itchy, and scaly.

*Diazepam, first marketed as Valium, is a medicine that counteracts anxiety. It may, I was to learn later, be used to induce memory loss during certain medical procedures, so I guess it was a good choice.

Dr D – THE PROBLEM WITH BREASTS

Most breast lumps are not cancerous but finding a lump must be one of the most frightening events in any woman's life. Sadly, one woman in seven will have breast cancer during their lifetime. Fortunately, the survival rate continues to improve and currently 85% of patients are cancer-free five years after being treated.

Before examining any patient with any breast centred symptom, I always told them that whatever I found, I would almost certainly be referring them for an X-ray, a mammogram. For a male doctor, examining a woman's breast is an invasive act and I was always aware that my expression was being scrutinised by my understandably anxious patient for any indication of what I had discovered, as well as any hint that I might be enjoying the manoeuvre. It is a complex situation for both parties.

On a female surgical ward round, soon after I became a clinical student, we stopped at the bed of a very attractive, healthy-looking woman of about 35 who had a very large breast lump, which was known to be benign. The consultant surgeon, who had an excellent bedside manner, asked the patient if all the students could examine her, as her problem raised an important issue. There wasn't time for us all to examine her at the time, so, as we moved on, he thanked her and got her agreement that the rest of us could come to see her later, which I did the following morning.

Successful advertising campaigns by amoral food companies had been so successful in persuading young mothers that breast feeding was primitive, and that bottle feeding was sophisticated, that, when my wife had our first daughter four years later, she was the only woman out of 15 in the post-natal ward who was breast feeding. This was despite the midwives and doctors' attempts to promote it.

Inevitably, these unemployed breasts became painfully engorged. Then the milk in the swollen ducts often became infected, and the abscesses that developed were often inappropriately treated with antibiotics, which halted the infection but left patients, like the one I was returning to examine, with large sterile abscesses. These only healed when the contents were drained through a small incision and a tube left in place to prevent fluid accumulating while the cavity healed up.

By the time I got to her bedside our patient had, unknown to me, established herself as the ward comedienne and, as I pulled the curtains around her bed, the ward fell silent. We had been taught that, if possible, it was better to examine breasts and the abdomen with patients in a supine position and the examiner sitting on the bed or next to it rather than standing up. This was preferable for the same reasons that make it harder to write standing up at a desk than sitting down.

No chair was easily available, so I sat on the edge of her bed.

When my feet were seen leaving the floor, she received an enthusiastic round of applause from her fellow patients.

"YOU can lie down if you like."

After a fairly cursory examination of the now famous lump, having declined her offer and had a brief battle with the curtains, I emerged to more applause and fled, red-faced to the relative safety of the ward sister's office.

"She got you too, did she?" said a grinning staff nurse. "Well, you won't do that again will you!"

Many years later, an equally statuesque, half-naked Swedish patient who was sitting on my couch waiting for a breast examination said, "Do you realise I'm paying you for this doctor?" There was no embarrassment this time.

Another patient of mine, while sitting on a hospital examination couch, was asked to raise her arms above her head, a routine part of breast examination, but the surgeon got distracted by something and, after a couple of minutes she enquired sweetly, "Why am I feeling that I have somehow become involved in an armed robbery?"

Although most of my patients saw me on a private basis, I always remained on the NHS list of GPs. I was often allocated patients who had experienced difficulty joining another practice. One day, a social worker brought along two black girls in their late teens who were doing nursing training in Worthing but living in a hostel in Hove and needed to register with a GP, which I was happy to arrange.

The social worker told me their horrifying histories. Both girls had seen their entire families murdered by the soldiers of a central African "liberation army". They had been abducted and forced into being sex slaves and cooks for this guerrilla group and raped repeatedly over many months.

Eventually the group was ambushed by government forces and most of the irregular soldiers, many of whom were only teenagers, had been killed in the shooting. The girls had survived with only minor injuries and been scooped up by a Catholic charity, which arranged their move to Britain.

A couple of months later, one of the girls came to see me, by herself. She had gained a bit of weight and looked well. Her command of English was very poor and heavily accented, but after my few opening remarks, which I suspect she did not fully understand, she said, "Doctor, I have pain in mah teets."

My immediate reaction was to think that she might not have avoided becoming pregnant during her recent ordeal, so I asked if her periods were regular, but she seemed not to understand.

I thought I had been told that she came from the Congo and would therefore understand French. So, I conducted a masterclass in Failed Communication.

My French "O" level days were long behind me and, as I was unable to remember the French word for pregnant, I thought it must derive from the Latin synonym popular with medics – "gravid".

My question "Etes vous en greve peut etre?" did not seem to help so assuming that my examining her would answer the question I gestured towards the couch and mimed the removal of her T-shirt.

It is hardly surprising that she looked utterly confused. She was being confronted by a tall white man patting his lower abdomen, suggesting she took off her clothes and asking, in an atrocious accent, if she was on strike.

A few moments later she gave a big smile of understanding and, pointing to her gleaming incisors, said "Not mah teets doctor, mah TEETS!"

I wasn't entirely surprised that I did not see her or her friend again; perhaps they moved to Worthing.

Dr R – A DAY TO REMEMBER

If you were neurotic like me and had an enormous fear of failure, there was an opportunity to qualify six months early, through a different examination board: Conjoint. LRCP MRCS*. I was in the unusual situation of being married while at medical school. Heather was now a primary school teacher in a lovely little state school in the middle of Highgate Village, North London. We were blessed to have accommodation, a two-bedroom house in the school grounds. We already had a child, Ben, aged 12 months and Heather was 6-7 weeks pregnant again when I went into my final exams spread over two days. I passed the first half on the Wednesday only to come home to find that my wife was bleeding very slightly, meaning she might be miscarrying. We called on Heather's mum from Sussex to support us while I went back the following day to complete my exams. I was to have the result that day. Pass or fail. This all happened in one of the colleges on Queen's Square in London. All the terrified students were gathered around in the basement. The smell emanating from the toilets was overpowering. Many were literally "shit scared" and suffering from the most awful nervous diarrhoea. The results were due at 2 o'clock in the afternoon; the mechanism of this delivery was not much short of torture. A secretary with a large book placed herself at the foot of a very impressive staircase and called out names in alphabetical order. She would tell you if you had passed or failed. If you were successful, you mounted the stairs with a certificate to be congratulated by a handful of academics. Failure meant turning around empty-handed to walk back into the mass of waiting students. Why the college chose a secretary who had quite a marked stutter for such a weighty task was beyond me. Imagine my experience.

"Brooks, Roderick John?"

"Yes."

"Date of birth."

"19/04/1947."

"You have pa pa pa pa pa pa PASSED." The stutter stretched into eternity.

I wanted to ask, "Are you sure?" but this wasn't the time or place to be mucking about. I rushed, or rather "flew" home, with the long-awaited status of being a doctor. Heather stood up to greet me, only to suffer a large haemorrhage. We padded her up and drove down to the New Charing Cross Hospital in Fulham. They were short-staffed, so I assisted at her D&C*. Quite a day! I was a doctor at last, but Heather was no longer pregnant.

---

*LRCP MRCS Licentiate of the Royal College of Physicians. Member of the Royal College of Surgeons

*D&C – Dilation and curettage is a procedure to remove tissue from inside the uterus (womb)

Dr D – THE EVENING ROUND

Life as a house doctor at Brighton General Hospital in the late 60s was quite tough. We usually managed to be off duty on alternate evenings but did not get much rest when we were on call. My memory is of spending most of the day on the ward, but we also had to dictate discharge letters, talk to relatives and conduct (well supervise) outpatient clinics. The one compulsory commitment was to do complete ward rounds twice a day. The morning round concentrated on adjusting or initiating treatment and organising investigations, whereas the evening session was a bit more relaxed. I thoroughly enjoyed talking to most of the patients but remember at least one exception. Mr Benson was a bad-tempered 72-year-old diabetic whose heavy smoking had reduced the blood supply to his legs to a trickle. The senior hospital physician, Dr Barrington Prowse, a good old-fashioned doctor, and a very courteous man, had warned him that his right leg might well become gangrenous, but he was suggesting a new treatment, administered intravenously, which might improve his condition if he also stopped smoking.

His left leg was wrapped up to keep it warm, in the hope that this would increase blood supply and encourage the same response in the other leg, which was exposed and being cooled by a fan. The theory was that the cooler the limb was, the less blood supply it would require. I had no difficulty inserting the needle and then the cannula into a large vein in his left arm. I connected this to a bottle of normal saline by a tube with a simple flow regulator. The patient grumbled incoherently as I did this and, in response, I told him to be patient and reinforced the "no smoking" diktat. Later that day the bottle of magic juice arrived; I put it in place of the Saline and set the flow rate so that the contents would be administered over the next 12 hours.

I made him my first call the next morning and asked if his leg felt any better.

"Of course, it doesn't, you bloody young fool – you put it on the wrong side."

I always found it rather endearing that many of the older patients in the female ward would spruce themselves up for their hoped-for visitors and for the doctors' evening round. They would wait, smiling and expectant, with their hair combed, teeth in, a touch of badly applied makeup, and a clean bed jacket. On one very hot summer evening, this scene was being enacted as I wandered from bed to bed. The old lady in bed seven, normally a rather quiet and passive old dear, was distinctly agitated.

"She's stolen my teeth," she said pointing to bed number eight.

"No," I said confidently "They're probably in your locker or in your bed."

"I tell you, she's nicked my dentures," she shouted.

I moved to the next patient who was lying down with the sheet up to her eyes.

"Have you seen Mrs Morton's teeth?"

No reply was needed because with a slow lowering of the sheet the mystery was solved. She was "wearing" two sets of dentures, one on top of the other, and an enormous grin!

Dr R – JUNIOR HOSPITAL DOCTOR DAYS (AND NIGHTS)

At the New Charing Cross Hospital, (where I worked in my first hospital post), the junior staff were invited to a lunchtime teaching session performed by the Professor of Pathology. I was a house surgeon at the time and had been assisting at an operation that morning. My boss had removed a suspicious lump from a young woman's breast and wanted to know the histology as soon as possible. I was able to have this specimen examined before the lecture and was eager to learn the result. On this lunch hour, some 30 of us were gathered together in one of the lecture theatres. I was hiding at the back of the room as usual, as I found these occasions intimidating. I am, or rather was, 6'3" so this wasn't always that easy. "Ah, I have an interesting case brought in by Dr Brooks, who hopefully is with us this morning?" Boomed the great man. I popped up a hand in confirmation. "I see you have marked this biopsy as 'E.R.G.E.N.T'." (He spelt the word out with dramatic intonation). This revelation produced a rumble of disloyal sniggers from my colleagues. It was many years later that I was to learn that I was dyslexic. No wonder I found everything so blooming hard during my career, especially pharmaceutical spellings. One thing that I did learn right from the start was that occasionally you had to take a risk, and humour was often a successful way of getting out of an embarrassing situation. "Yes Sir, I spelt it that way to catch your attention." This brought a smile to the faces of most of the ensemble but not that of the professor, so I guess it was only a partial success.

Around this time, my wife became pregnant again and we had a second child while I was still working as a House Surgeon. However, during my wife's pregnancy, my mother-in-law, aged 49, died unexpectedly, with complications from influenza. This completely disrupted our lives as my pregnant wife gave up her teaching post in Highgate and moved down to Sussex to support her father and two siblings, aged 16 and 10. This meant I lost my accommodation and had to move into a hospital room provided in a tower block next to the new Charing Cross hospital in Fulham.

On completion of my first house job, I turned down a medical house job at the Cross for a post at Brighton General Hospital. Again, I was provided with the basic hospital living accommodation, but, when not on call I at least could spend some time with my family, eight miles away in Hassocks.

At Brighton General Hospital, just two of us very "inexperienced" junior doctors covered the medical wards 24 hours a day. A typical day was 8am–8pm. On top of that we alternated emergency cover every second night with added basic ward work every second weekend. You do the math: the week including the weekend duties was 144 hours, and the "easy" week without the weekend was 84 hours. This averaged out at 114 hours a week. A working week in most occupations at that time was 38 hours, exactly 1/3 of 114 hours; and we weren't allowed to strike for better conditions. However, I did learn a lot, and had to learn very quickly, but at great cost to family life. I hardly ever saw my children and, when I did, I was too exhausted to enjoy my time with them.

When I finished my second house job, I was qualified to enter General Practice if I wished. However, a 3-year course to prepare doctors better for General Practice had emerged. Soon it was going to be compulsory to complete what was called The Vocational GP Training Scheme (VTS), so I joined the Brighton branch. I acquired a hospital bungalow with two bedrooms in the grounds of Brighton General Hospital and there we lived, the four of us, for two years until I was finally able to buy my first home, a two-bed end of terrace house in a quiet cul-de-sac in the Kemptown part of Brighton. No more rented accommodation for me, or so I thought!

My lovely dad sadly and very unexpectedly died of a heart attack when he was 60. He was a great supporter of me both academically and in terms of sport. At the time, I was halfway through my vocational training, and he wasn't there to celebrate me finally achieving my goal of entering General Practice. I had always wanted to take up two season tickets for Brighton and Hove Albion Football Club and share Saturday home matches with him. We might even have gone to the odd away match.

My older brother by four years, returned home to live with my mother after 25 years in the RAF. He had never married and to this day remains single and childless. While I was a house surgeon at the New Charing Cross Hospital in London, my mother was admitted onto my ward for surgery and a subsequent course of radiotherapy. I can't say I welcomed this development, as my relationship with my mother was challenging to say the least. Unfortunately, despite all going well, she unexpectedly coughed up a lump of fresh blood a few months later. We feared the worst and she was readmitted, this time to Brighton General Hospital (BGH), where I was now working as a house physician. The female medical ward at BGH was an open ward except for one side-room that was allocated to my mother as a courtesy to me. Despite all this amazing personal treatment she received, which was all down to me, I found her very demanding and irritating. I had enough on my plate to cope with, what with it being the winter and in the middle of a flu epidemic. We were experiencing many deaths on the ward. The routine for a death was to pull the curtains around the bed of the deceased; the porters then turned up with a tin coffin on rollers and removed the body. One Wednesday morning two porters duly turned up to remove one of our deceased patients. In a moment of madness, I pointed to the side-room where my mother was having a nap, only for her to wake up with two men trying to lift her out of her bed. Needless to say, the porters were deeply traumatised by this experience and never really spoke to me after that. As for my mother, when she did eventually die 20 years later, my brother (with whom I also had and still have a challenging relationship) was the only beneficiary of her will.

I missed the following event and only heard about it from a traumatised junior nurse. Apparently, the evening before, she had been on her own in the male medical ward at Brighton General Hospital. An African man had been admitted that afternoon with abdominal pain, not thought to be surgical. He was on holiday from his native country and had only arrived in the UK two days before. As this poor girl was passing his bed, he suddenly vomited on the floor in front of her. This didn't particularly bother her, otherwise she wouldn't have been training to be a nurse. It was when she saw a twelve inches long tapeworm wriggling "towards her" that she freaked. She admitted to having screamed and run out of the ward shouting for help. I thought it was a little unkind of the sister-in-charge to reprimand her for unprofessional conduct. I have to say I was quite relieved not to have been working that evening, as my reaction might well have been the same.

I also didn't witness the next incident, which happened to the counsellor attached to the hospital. She enjoyed robust health and rarely sought medical advice. One morning, about half an hour after eating breakfast, she developed acute abdominal pain, which became severe, culminating in a bout of non-productive retching. She was becoming quite desperate and was about to dial 999 for an ambulance, when she vomited. The stomach pain subsided almost immediately. When she had recovered sufficiently to start cleaning up her mess, she noticed among the undigested food, a tiny mouse! By this time the counsellor was considering having counselling herself. However, she did think that maybe the creature had somehow got into the manufacturing process of her freeze-dried muesli, and when it had arrived in her stomach it had rehydrated, explaining her body's dramatic reaction. I have to admit, it put me off breakfast cereals for a long time.

Dr D – OFF THE BOOZE!

One morning I was called out of a surgical out-patient clinic to see a man who had just arrived on the ward and was very ill. He was a slim man, aged about 55, smelling strongly of alcohol and tobacco smoke. He was also pale and sweating and not very communicative. Any movement and certainly any attempt to examine the site of the pain, his stomach, caused him to grunt and tense up. This situation is referred to as "an acute abdomen" and he was immediately prepared for surgery. We later learned that he was a rep for a locally based wholesale drinks company called Findlater Prentis and clearly enjoyed a little too much sampling of the hooch he was selling on his round of pubs and off-licences.

Once his abdomen was opened, the cause of this poor man's pain became immediately apparent. An ulcer in his stomach had perforated allowing its contents to drain into the abdominal cavity, causing a chemical peritonitis. In this case, the chemicals involved were gastric acid, bile, coffee and Scotch, a highly irritating cocktail. The ulcer was sewn up and, after the escaped fluid had been sucked out of the cavity and it had been washed with a couple of litres of sterile fluid, the incision was stitched up and a drainage tube left in place. His general condition was poor so instead of returning to his bed, he was transferred to the Intensive Care Unit.

Three days later, he was back in his bed having made good progress but in a confused and very agitated state.

In addition to the abdominal drain, he had an intravenous drip in his left arm, a bladder catheter, and a tube through his nose to prevent the build-up of fluid in his stomach, which might otherwise put pressure on his healing wound. He was doing his best to get rid of all these essential tubes and, after the nurses had twice managed to replace the naso-gastric tube and I had twice reinserted the intravenous cannula attached to the drip set, it finally dawned on me that he was having DTs.

The hospital pharmacist, who rarely saw any of the clinical ward staff, was delighted to see me and happily agreed to my suggestion that he supply my patient with some alcohol in the intravenous fluid we were giving him. Half an hour later he appeared on the ward cradling a litre bottle of sterile fluid laced with the equivalent of about a third of a bottle of spirits, with which I immediately replaced the existing drip fluid.

By this time, the patients' arms were firmly tied to the cot sides put in place to stop him falling out of bed as he cursed and thrashed about. Feeling there was not much to be gained by temerity I briefly fully opened the flow valve allowing a cupful of the alcoholic fluid into his system. The effect was miraculous; within a few minutes, he was calm, quiet, and then fell asleep, much to everyone's relief.

Over the following days, we gradually reduced his invisible alcohol intake; a week later, I asked how he felt.

"I'm feeling pretty good, thank you doctor."

He leaned towards me and, in a confiding tone of voice, told me proudly that he hadn't had a drink for over a week, the first time for years.

I glanced at his drip but decided against contradicting him.

One of the frustrations of hospital medicine is that junior doctors are much less likely to know the long-term outcomes of their patients.

I can only hope that my man ended up as a staunch member of AA and lived a long and sober life.

Dr R – A&E, YOU CAN'T MAKE IT UP

I loved my nine months stint in the A&E department at the Royal Sussex County Hospital in the late 1970s. Brighton has such a mixed culture with every conceivable ethnic group and sexual orientation. There were usually around four senior house officers manning the department. There were several examination rooms for minor accidents and illnesses. All examinations were carried out in the presence of a female chaperone, whose role was basically to organise patients if further investigations were required – X-rays, bloods etc. – and to "police" any inappropriate behaviour. Nearby was the doctors' rest room with basic coffee/tea facilities and, most importantly, a TV. If there was an important football or rugby match on, all the junior doctors would gather around the "box" until the A&E department was overrun with patients. We would then be dragged away from the game (there was no pause button in those days) by the chaperones, to sort out the patients, which we did as quickly as possible, then returned to whatever we were watching. On one busy Saturday evening with a combination of multiple casualties and a heavy sporting timetable on the TV, a couple of gay guys presented themselves with an injury. One of them had apparently slipped on the pavement and twisted his right foot. On examination, sure enough he was presenting with a swollen painful ankle. I shot him off for an X-ray and saw him with his partner and my chaperone about an hour later. I couldn't see any obvious fracture on the X-ray, although I must admit radiology wasn't one of my strengths. My diagnosis was a simple sprain that required strapping and pain relief. I explained all this to the injured man. However, it was at that point that I offered some more helpful advice. I asked him if he had a pouffe* at home. If he had, I suggested that when he got home, it would help with the swelling of the ankle if he elevated his injured foot by resting it on his pouffe. The chaperone, unhelpfully, found it necessary to abandon the examination room as she had some difficulty controlling her shoulders. This left me, inexplicably at the time, with two rather hostile young men. I wished them good evening, went off to save some more lives and thought nothing more about it. I worked through the night, had Sunday off, and was back on duty on Monday morning, only to be summoned to the office by the head of the department*, as there had been a complaint about my conduct with a patient over the weekend. It turned out that the chap with the twisted ankle had misinterpreted my use of the word "pouffe" as homophobic*. It was the 70s and I was very young; I had to actually ask what "homophobic" meant. When all had been explained to me, I began to understand how this unfortunate situation had arisen. I was just given a mild slap on the wrist. However, as I closed the door, and walked down the corridor suitably chastised, I could hear a poorly suppressed chuckle emanating from his office.

In Casualty, I repeatedly got caught out by abdominal pain presentations. I do remember two well-covered women, one aged

16, and the other aged 45, who both complained of lower stomach cramps and a watery vaginal discharge. Within 30 minutes, and with absolutely no help from me, one delivered a seven-and-a-half-pound baby boy and the other delivered twins! Both denied sexual contact with anyone, ever!

Timothy was a well-spoken florist, with an interesting moustache, who presented with what he described as a "noisy stomach". Examination with a stethoscope did, in fact, reveal a constant humming sound. On the operating table, after opening the colon, we found a rather splendid vibrator, but none of us in the operating theatre knew, or we pretended not to know, how to turn the blooming thing off. Of course, the most junior female nurse was elected to return the object back, FULLY STERILISED, to the patient after he regained consciousness.

Nigel, aged 25 years of age, kept me up all night another time, trying to work out what was wrong with him in his semi-comatose state. At 6 am, he suddenly got up and walked out of the department, apparently symptom free. Four hours later, my having had exactly nineteen and a half minutes sleep, he turned up and promptly collapsed in the waiting room where I was working as a GP locum (moonlighting to pay the mortgage). The receptionist summoned me in a panic. However, I recognised this young man and whispered in his ear that I was just going to pop into my consulting room to retrieve my 9-inch-long steel proctoscope* and explained in some detail what I was going to do with it. The "patient" was gone when I returned a few moments later. The receptionist thought I was wonderful. I never told her the reason why he left so abruptly.

London had turned out to be the perfect place for me to study. At an early stage in my training, I wanted to be a GP in a busy city environment. Brighton was in many ways a mini-London by the sea. Everything that you can imagine and more passes through Casualty, including countless drug addicts in all kinds of despair. I remember a particular young girl who had developed a nasty abscess on her leg that needed draining urgently under a general anaesthetic. However, the senior anaesthetist on call was unable to find a vein to put her to sleep. "Here, let me have a go," she chirped, and in seconds she was successful. What a waste of a skill, I thought at the time. Unfortunately, this newly acquired skill was ultimately going to kill her, and it did, six months later.

On a lighter note, a great friend of mine who was the surgical registrar on duty was called to Casualty where a delicate young man in his twenties had reported an unusual accident. Apparently, he had been having supper with his partner in the kitchen of their flat, when, on sitting down on a stool, a fork disappeared up his bottom. This is not a common accident but, on the other hand, not completely unheard of. Sure enough, an X-ray confirmed the foreign body and after lot of skilful activity with another proctoscope, a fork was retrieved, attached to about six inches of string with some hardy Sellotape.

*A pouffe is a cushioned footstool or low seat with no back.

*The Head of the A&E Department was the Senior Orthopaedic Surgeon, an amiable chap, who, it was rumoured, was having an affair with one, or maybe two of the night sisters. I have to say in the poor chap's defence that there was absolutely no evidence for these malicious gossips.

*For any reader as naïve as I was, "homophobic" means, "having or showing a dislike of or prejudice against homosexual people." This was bloody ridiculous, as, at the time, I didn't know any homosexual people, male or female.

*Proctoscope: a rigid, metal surgical instrument approximately 6 inches in length used to examine the anal cavity, rectum, or sigmoid colon, or all three if you are lucky.

Dr D – FAROUK THE INCOMPETENT

When "on call", all the junior doctors at the Brighton General Hospital (BGH) had the use of their own bedroom in "K" Block; most of us, including married couples, lived there permanently, with food, laundry and cleaning supplied by two lovely women, Edie, and Ruth. The junior orthopaedic surgeons had almost all been trained abroad, mostly in India, and they were slightly better paid than the rest of us. They were mostly friendly, very competent, and clearly ambitious. The least popular and wealthiest was the solitary Farouk, who was supported with generous grants from the Egyptian Government but was humourless and entirely incompetent. Unable to carry out the simplest tasks expected of him, he depended on us his peers to compensate for his inadequacies.

One evening, when he and I were on call to our respective wards, an elderly lady, who had undergone surgery for a fractured neck of femur, lost consciousness as a result of blood loss and needed immediate blood transfusion. The staff nurse had taken blood samples to estimate the degree of anaemia and for X-matching with the blood to be transfused and had already sent them to the lab before Farouk was summoned to the ward. Looking a bit anxious, he disappeared behind drawn curtains with instructions to set up an intravenous drip to administer an infusion of plasma as an interim measure.

At this time, the plasma was freeze-dried and needed to be diluted with sterile saline solution.

When Farouk had failed to reappear after about 15 minutes, the staff nurse went to investigate. She found that Farouk had opened the plastic bottle of saline and the packet of dried plasma but, instead of combining the two into a liquid for intravenous infusion, he was trying to spoon powdered plasma into the old lady's mouth and get her to swallow it down with sips of the saline. Eventually the blood for transfusion arrived and the old lady, who had no idea how unorthodox her treatment had been, made a full recovery.

Farouk probably ended up as an administrator, I sincerely hope he was never allowed to practice any form of surgery more demanding than podiatry.

Dr R – GERIATRICS AND DERMATOLOGY

During my BSc elective* I was awarded a grant to study in a research department in La Jolla, California. The project was about Tay-Sachs Disease* and it was to become a vital contribution to my CV*. Five years later, I had an extremely important interview for the junior houseman post at Brighton General Hospital. It was all going reasonably well until at the end of a 30-minute grilling by six consultants; the very last question came from the local Consultant Dermatologist, a certain Pat Hall-Smith.

"Brooks, I see here that you took part in some Tay-Sachs research."

"Yes sir," I said nervously.

"Isn't that the condition formerly known as ....?" He went on to quote a long and largely unpronounceable Latin name followed by a mini lecture about the condition. (He had clearly read up about it the night before)

"Yes sir." I was very nervous now.

"And Brooks, what was your sole purpose in studying this interesting condition?"

As I had not actually turned up at the Research Department very often and had to think up something, I said, "Well sir, the research unit was very close to the beach, and I had travelled over to California with my girlfriend. I must admit that I spent most of my time learning to surf in the ocean."

This produced rather a long pause in the interview followed by, "Do you know Brooks, if I was in your situation, I think I would have done exactly the same thing."

End of interview. I got the job!

I got to know Pat Hall-Smith really well over the next few years and we had a lot of fun together. He looked after a few beds on the medical ward of Brighton General Hospital that were mostly occupied by patients with enormous and weeping chronic varicose* ulcers of the legs. I never quite got to grips with the treatment and left most of it to the highly competent nurses. After his daily ward round, I would accompany him to the Outpatient Department, a couple of minutes' walk from the ward. At that time, I lived in Bungalow 2 with my family, and we had to pass it en route to the morning clinic. We seemed to see hundreds of patients, but it all worked well and provided a good service to the local community and beyond. I'm not sure how it all started but it became a working tradition to pop into my accommodation for a quick, but often large gin and tonic before ploughing into a sea of patients for the next four hours.

I used to do a lot of moonlighting when I could fit it in, and any dermatological problem that I came across I would simply add to the outpatient list for the next morning. When I entered General Practice and had a skin problem during a morning surgery, I could always telephone Pat directly and he would see him, or her, at the end of his morning session. What a service!

When Pat retired, the incoming Consultant Dermatologist was

not quite as accommodating, to say the least. I bumped into Pat at a post-graduate lunchtime meeting sometime later while he was chatting to half a dozen or so similarly retired colleagues. I thought that I should not miss the opportunity to thank him personally and especially in front of this small group. After I had spoken at some length about my gratitude he reached into his pocket and gave me a 10 pence coin and said, "Why thank you, Professor Brooks (he always addressed me as "Professor" in public), why don't you go and treat yourself to a cup of tea." His comic timing was perfect, and I have used the same ploy on the rare occasions anyone thanked me for a particular service. I never quite pulled it off with the same aplomb, though.

The post-graduate centre at Brighton General Hospital provided an excellent library and research centre, together with good catering and lecture theatre facilities. It was frequently used for medical conferences and provided a base for the GP vocational training scheme among many other functions. At least every week there would be a lunchtime post-grad lecture given by one of the consultants and lunch was often provided by one of the pharmaceutical companies. The audience was, on the whole, split between the regular forward-thinking younger GPs, and the usual suspects of retired or semi-retired GPs. I don't think it is unkind to say that the latter came for a chat, a free meal, and a snooze in the lecture theatre afterwards. It became a sort of club for this group. Traditionally, the front row was occupied by a regular turn out of senior female GPs, mostly single or widowed. The steps in the lecture theatre were fairly steep and this may have accounted for this. Pat Hall-Smith was well aware of his clientele on the occasions he was giving a lecture. He would mostly back up his talk with an eclectic array of slides, mostly rashes looking to me much the same. He would invite the audience to identify a certain lump or discolouration on the skin. Without fail, he would suddenly provide the most graphic and horrifying slide of an ulcer on an enormous hairy and pendulous penis. He would then blatantly look along the front row of females. "Dr Mary, any ideas how you would deal with this condition?" His ability to keep a bland expression on his face was masterful but the mischievous twinkle in his eyes always gave him away. Pat is no longer with us, and he is sorely missed as one of Brighton's great medical characters.

Pat and I often talked over coffee after a punishing outpatient session. We talked about my hopes for the future and, in the following years he was a great friend especially when I was pursuing my career in General Practice in Brighton. He leaned into me once and told me in confidence a story about travelling through London to get to a dermatological viva held in one of the colleges. This was to form a vital part of his Royal College of Medicine exam. He admitted to great anxiety on the day, as he had no idea what to expect. While walking through one of London's parks close to the college he got into conversation with an elderly gentleman. This old boy, it turned out, was to be one of the volunteer exhibits for one of the examinations going on in the college that particular day. He was eager to tell Pat all about his rare condition and how the students rarely got it right. Pat admitted he had listened with some enthusiasm. Three arduous hours later Pat was coming to the end of his examination when, in the last bed, he was presented with his new friend from the park. Throughout the whole 30 minutes Pat spent with him, the patient did not give away any hint of a prior meeting. However, on shaking the patient's hand before leaving, he noticed the faintest of winks. What a good sport. Pat passed his exam, and the rest is history. It was meant to be, I guess.

During my six-month post as an SHO* in Geriatrics and Dermatology* I was still living in Bungalow 2 with my wife and two pre-school children. I could actually see some of my geriatric patients from our bedroom window – convenient, sure, but I felt I could never quite get away from the job. I also found myself popping into the wards at all hours when I was off duty simply because I could. Out of sight, out of mind clearly wasn't going to work here. The bungalow was heated off the same system as the rest of the hospital, so we were never cold and shared our home with several million cockroaches of all sizes! I can still hear that familiar crunch as I padded into the kitchen at night to get a drink. They could really run when you turned on the lights! Next door, Bungalow 1, was never occupied during my stay at Brighton General, for some reason. That was to our advantage, as we shared a garden. In my attempt to be the perfect family man, I bought a couple of gerbils for the children to "look after". I built a large cage in the garden for them to run around in. The hospital's resident foxes however, developed a fondness for them too and that was the end of that adventure. I didn't learn from my mistake as several years later, when I was in General Practice with a lovely house and a walled garden, I decided to buy a couple of dwarf rabbits for the children to play with. I think I was conned in the pet shop because, a year later, these baby rabbits were anything but "dwarf"! They used to have the run of the garden when we were home and then be brought in at night. However, as they grew older and faster, we increasingly found it difficult to catch the blooming animals and occasionally they had a sleepover in the garden. Eventually another fox decided to join them (perhaps it was the same one from the hospital) and that was that, again!

As Bungalow 1 was always empty, we put up friends from London there from time to time, boasting of having a second home in Brighton, albeit the one next door. I religiously took the British Medical Journal (BMJ) every week as it provided a useful tool if I could not sleep; it always worked, usually after page 2! I never threw them out as they hadn't really been read, so I stored them next door in the hope that when I was less busy, I would systematically go through them until I caught up with the current issue. Much to my relief, a sewer burst in Bungalow 1 while we were away for the weekend and completely contaminated the entire collection, so once again, that was that.

My workload for Geriatrics was the least demanding of all my jobs in hospital. Dermatology was mostly outpatients and that was always good fun, largely due to the extremely charismatic consultant. However, I did have a bit of a scare when asked by a Consultant Geriatrician to perform a sternal bone marrow biopsy. I had never done one, nor seen one performed; but I was not going to admit to that. At the end of the ward round, I did a bit of reading up, (This is so easy now as one can view it on YouTube and off you go!) I grabbed the most senior sister and set about the task. After injecting a few drops of local anaesthetic, I started drilling into the sternum with some enthusiasm. Whether the drill was blunt or not, I don't know, but it appeared to be taking ages and I was hungry as it was past my lunchtime. However, suddenly, the drill took a downward lurch of what felt like at least an inch. I did a quick calculation and reckoned that the intrusive metal had penetrated to the heart of the unsuspecting patient. I gingerly removed the offending instrument and instinctively popped a thumb over the neat hole in the bone to contain the release of any diverted blood. It felt like I had just popped the cork of a champagne bottle, so I kept my thumb over the top to avoid spraying everyone and everything in the vicinity. I don't mind being sprayed with champagne, as it happens, but blood is a different thing all together. In an attempt to assess the damage, I slowly eased my thumb off his sternum and blow me, nothing happened. The patient had not lost consciousness, so that was a good sign. I did manage to acquire a specimen of bone marrow, which, despite all my efforts, was reported to be normal by the laboratory. I placed a plaster over the hole and off I went to lunch. I couldn't face the tomato soup, however, as it reminded me of the blood bath that could have been. On reflection, the drill had simply gone through the outer layer of the bone and reached the intended target, the marrow. All these traumas are character-building, I thought as I picked at my NHS salad.

*Elective: an optional course of study or, in my case, a great chance to get a suntan and get to know my girlfriend better

*Tay Sachs Disease is a disease marked by the accumulation of 62 gangliosides due to hexosaminidase A deficiency – I hope that is helpful!

*CV or Curriculum Vitae (Latin I think) is a brief account of a person's education, qualifications, and previous occupations, typically sent with a job application.

*Varicose Ulcers are a type of chronic sore on the leg or foot, not always easy to treat and not to be recommended.

*SHO Senior House Officer: an excellent opportunity to treat the Junior House Officers as badly as I had been mistreated.

*Geriatrics is a specialty that focuses on elderly wrinkly patients.

*Dermatology focuses on both young and old people with wrinkly skin.

Dr D – LABOUR INTENSIVE

My third and last hospital job was as an Obstetrics and Gynaecology House Surgeon, and it was a largely enjoyable one. The trainee midwives attended most of the daytime deliveries that were considered unlikely to be problematic, leaving the doctors to cope with the predictably difficult ones and emergencies. We listened to foetal hearts with a stethoscope that looked like a plastic wine glass with a hollow stem and tried to become skilled at examining the abdomen to assess the position of the foetus. The ultrasound scanner, which removed many uncertainties about the baby's condition, was invented in Glasgow in 1958 but was not in general hospital use until the 1970s.

The senior midwives, who on this unit were almost all elderly spinsters, were competent but not very tolerant. Changes in social and sexual activities were disrupting their routines and challenging their religious beliefs. As the 1960s progressed and sexual activity increased, especially among the young, but sadly without a concurrent awareness that semen was an important component of conception, underage and unplanned pregnancies became much more common.

My time as a trainee obstetrician coincided with the passage through Parliament of David Steel's 1968 Abortion Bill, which was long overdue but came too late to help the frightened teenagers I was assisting. These girls were often terrified of labour, which produced a baby that was immediately taken away from them and put up for adoption. Many had been subjected to parental disapproval, ostracised by some elements of society, and did not receive a very sympathetic approach from the midwives they encountered. Trying to do a forceps delivery with a frightened, screaming 15-year-old, too out of control to inhale the analgesic gas, was often more like wrestling than obstetrics.

The gynaecological surgery lacked the range of general surgery and probably revealed fewer unexpected conditions. One excited surgeon was keen to show a rather indolent anaesthetist the bizarre pair of ovaries he had just removed. Reluctantly the gas man shuffled round to the other side of the surgical drapes, to where I was standing holding a retractor, looked at the severed organs and then shuffled back, grunted, and then said sarcastically "Is there no end to Nature's diversity?" Then he returned to his crossword puzzle.

On one occasion, a girl in her 20s, needing a D and C, arrived at the theatre on a trolley and was lifted onto the operating table, where the anaesthetist administered his magic drugs. As soon as she was unconscious, the theatre nurse removed the girl's paper underpants to reveal a fine display of bright green pubic hair above which was a neat tattoo "Keep off the grass"!

It was sadly ironic that my time doing this job coincided with our own obstetric problems. In the summer of 1968, my then fiancée had wisely decided to accompany her parents and two younger sisters to Rio de Janeiro when her father was appointed Air and

Naval attaché at our embassy there, leaving me to do some much-needed studying. I reluctantly moved out of my flat in Highbury and into the small residential block on the Guy's campus known as Sophie's, where I did put my head down with good enough effect to pass the Conjoint final exam, which qualified me to apply for a houseman hospital job. We got married in the following February and, after a second round of exams that earned me a degree, we headed for Brighton and my first job – as a medical house officer with an income of £600 p.a.

My very tolerant wife had to swap the hedonistic pleasures of Copacabana Beach and modelling for a French couture house, for lonely evenings in K Block watching TV while waiting in the doctors' mess in case I managed to make an appearance. Over the next year, we had the disappointment of her having a couple of early spontaneous abortions, neither of which prepared her for the horrors of a miscarriage at 22 weeks. This involved a long, painful premature labour with no hope, in those days, of the baby's survival. This resulted in the birth of a perfect, tiny but dead boy, which was a shattering experience and one from which she never completely recovered. It was only when our first daughter was born with no problems a year later that she fully reacted to the disaster by developing a severe post-natal depression.

At this time, mental illnesses of all kinds were not much understood or discussed outside medical circles. The patient's misery and the sense of exclusion felt by those around them did not elicit much support from friends or even some family members.

Dr R – OBSTETRICS AND GYNAECOLOGY

The obstetrics and gynaecology medical school training was great fun overall. It was quite late in my training that I learned that my boss was a gynaecologist and not a vaginacologist as my 'father-in-law' had thought! The professor of the department was quite a smooth likeable chap, always ready to give us some gem to carry through our careers. One of his most memorable pieces of advice came when a pregnant patient asked what he thought the gender of their unborn child was. This was before scans became routine and readily available. He would always wait until the pregnancy had advanced to at least 30 weeks, and then make a lengthy external examination of the swollen abdomen, finishing up with an equally unnecessary long listen to the foetal heartbeat. He would announce with a flourish that the pregnancy would result in a baby boy. He would then inform the patient that he would write in the patient's notes to that effect. However, in the notes he would boldly write, SEX – GIRL, the opposite to what he had so confidently predicted. Some weeks later, when the woman reappeared in the post-natal clinic with her child, she could be among the 50% who thought the professor was extremely clever in knowing the sex of the child while still in the womb. The other half, however, returned a little disappointed at the clinician's misdiagnosis. The professor would then refer to his notes and show the patient what he had written. Outrageous, I thought at the time, but I was young. I was extremely tempted to use it when I finally made it into General Practice but never had the courage.

During my time learning obstetrics, I was farmed out, along with a good friend of mine, Harry, to a peripheral hospital just off the North Circular Road in London. We were pretty much left to get on with it and it was not without its near misses and tragedies.

One time, Harry, having taken too long to scrub up for a routine delivery, turned around only just in time to catch the new-born as it was propelled out of the woman's contracting uterus. He had been a wicketkeeper for his old school cricket team and this particular skill came in very handy!

The following week, a young Indian woman was admitted in advanced labour. Unfortunately, she did not speak any English and had come unaccompanied. Much to our distress, we delivered a stillborn girl and were unable to revive her. I think the poor child had been dead a few days. Harry and I were incredibly inexperienced, and we had very little back-up on the ward. We did not know how to inform the poor woman of her tragedy and eventually showed the mother her deceased baby, as we simply could not fathom an alternative. I think, by her reaction, that she wasn't altogether surprised that things had gone wrong. It was a bleak moment for all of us, and one that I have never forgotten and often think about. On a more cheerful note, I will always remember the thrill of assisting at my first delivery of twins, both healthy, thank goodness, and very noisy!

Episiotomies* were almost routine in the 1970s. I found it

extremely unpleasant inserting a large pair of scissors into the vagina of a distressed woman and actually cutting through the stretched flesh. I cannot imagine what it must be like for the patient. Well, I can, but I don't want to dwell on it. The readers may also choose not to, as he/she may well have their own memory to reflect on. When the delivery was all over, and the placenta safely removed from the womb, it was my job to sew up the wound and return the vagina to its former beauty. I remember vividly peering into this bloody mess thinking, where do I start? If you don't panic and try to remember the anatomy, it is actually quite simple (he says completely from a bloke's point of view!) but nobody is going to thank you if you sew it up too tightly. Or are they?

When I qualified, I worked under an extremely pleasant gynaecologist, Mr Herbert Melville, who was gentle and kind with patients and staff alike. I remember assisting him at a routine D&C* and being allowed to dilate the cervix with the appropriate instrument. However, the probe continued its journey through the roof of the uterus as if it was butter. Clearly, to my horror, I had successfully perforated the poor woman's womb at my first attempt. Fortunately for both of us, the laparoscopy* that was performed immediately (and certainly not by me) revealed no damage or leakage. She was sent back to the ward and told what had happened. Then a repeat D&C was booked in for the following week. This time, Mr Melville performed the operation and blow me if he didn't perforate the roof of the womb as well. He then made the decision to perform an abdominal hysterectomy*; that seemed to me rather drastic at the time, but who was I to know. The uterus was sent off to the laboratory for examination, and the *histology later came back with the diagnosis of Choriocarcinoma*. How rare was that? Perhaps my perforation had done her a favour, as this diagnosis was thus made early and I believe she responded to treatment and did very well.

Only a week after the perforation incident, I was assisting Mr Melville once again. This time, my contribution to the operation was largely verbal. I wanted all operations to be over as soon as possible as I was 6ft 3ins tall (a little less now) and most surgeons were a few inches shorter than me. Hence the operating table was always set too low for my comfort. I have a similar problem with ironing boards now! The result was that, at the end of an operating session, I suffered from chronic backache. This particular operation was a straightforward abdominal hysterectomy for one of the hospital sisters with fibroids*.

Mr Melville was pointing out various parts of the anatomy as he was going along with special reference to the ureters*. If you cut one of those, the peritoneum* doesn't like having urine splashed over, it. "Sir," I asked, "have you ever mistakenly cut a ureter?"

"Just the once Rod," he replied. "Twice now, actually," as his scalpel neatly severed the right ureter. There is often said to be a "built-in-buggeration factor" when medics are dealing with colleagues – and how true is that, as this operation turned out to be one of them. The nursing sister, did very well, however; otherwise, it could have been a lot worse. You would have thought Mr Melville would not have let me anywhere near his operating sessions after that, but he did, and the rest of my six months with him was largely uneventful. It wasn't much later, when looking after my wife's pregnancy he was informed, as a courtesy to a colleague, that she had gone into labour and her cervix was almost fully dilated. This was on a Sunday afternoon. He duly arrived 20 minutes later in his gardening clothes. He scrubbed up, delivered Freddie, congratulated us both and off he went back to his garden. I wonder if a junior hospital doctor's wife would be treated so kindly now. I hope so, but I'm not holding my breath.

When I finally finished my Vocational Training Scheme and entered General Practice, I looked forward to having my own antenatal clinic. It was such a joy to spend a morning with a bunch of basically healthy, albeit uncomfortable women. I was always slightly in awe of the hugeness of these ladies as they approached term. I had a routine with them. A quick chat while I was checking their urine sample for sugar and protein. A help up on to the examination couch where I did their BP, sitting up, then gently lowering them down so that I could examine the abdomen and listen to the foetal heart.

Having helped them up again, I would return to my desk to write up my notes while the patient sorted herself out. Usually, pregnancies advanced with little intervention from the doctor. "Masterly Inactivity," it is commonly called – a term my wife frequently mutters. However, on one particular morning I did get into a bit of a muddle. I had been up most of the night on call "saving lives" and I came into my surgery particularly exhausted. One of my regular, 20-something, and quite plump female patients came in to see me the following morning complaining of a severe frontal headache. I popped her up on the coach to check her BP and, in a flash, I had her lying down with her skirt pulled up to her chest to reveal her abdomen. While I was prodding away, she asked me why I was examining her stomach for a headache. I asked her what day it was. It was a Wednesday, but I had thought it was a Thursday, which was when I had my antenatal clinic. She laughed so much that her headache disappeared. She thought I was wonderful!

By the mid-80s, I was really enjoying General Practice and had a manageable antenatal following. I didn't have the anxiety of home births, as all our babies were delivered at The Royal Sussex Country Hospital in Brighton. I had been in practice for almost a decade and had had no disasters to date. The postnatal clinic was thus a joy. Not all babies, including my own, are the most beautiful creatures in the world. "Isn't he lovely doctor?" the mother would say, proudly holding up yet another wrinkly little prize for me to coo over. "What an interesting little face he has, certainly full of character," I replied with genuine honesty.

Jennifer was a 21-year young lady: a hairdresser, who was married to a painter and decorator. They lived in a council house on one of Brighton's estates and were saving up to buy their first home. This was their first pregnancy, and all was going well until, in her 30th week, she started to produce a little protein in her urine and her blood pressure became marginally elevated. She now required careful monitoring in case she developed pre-eclampsia*, a condition that puts the health of mother and unborn baby at risk. I arranged to see her the following week but unfortunately developed retinitis* of my right eye and was off work for six weeks. On my return, one of my receptionists informed me that Jennifer was on the phone and wanted to speak to me. She had had a stillbirth in my absence and wanted me to tell her how this had happened. This was awful news for me on my first day back, and I was able to see her before my evening surgery. I had allowed an hour so neither of us was to feel rushed. Jennifer came alone and, between us, we were able to unpick the events of the last few weeks of her pregnancy. Basically, her proteinuria and hypertension had not been monitored sufficiently in my absence, and she had developed *PET (pre-eclampsia toxaemia), with a tragic result.

She knew that I had just returned from sick leave. Looking down at her Lloyd George Folder of medical notes, in front of me, I noticed that she was registered with me, and not one of my partners. My contract with her and the National Health Service was to be responsible for her medical care, 24 hours a day, 7 days a week and 365 days a year. In my absence, I am obliged to put in my place, another registered doctor to continue my contractual duties. I explained this to her and said that, even though I had been on sick leave, I hadn't put in place sufficient safeguards for her and her baby's wellbeing. I said that I was deeply sorry for that, and I must take responsibility for what has happened. I will never forget her reply, even though this was about 35 years ago. "That's all I wanted to hear, Doctor. My husband told me to come and see you. He said that none of you doctors would want to deliberately hurt me." Some people are so generous and decent; it's a privilege to look after them. She smiled, shook hands with me and off she went. Four months later, she was pregnant again and asked me to look after her antenatal care! This time the outcome was perfect. The advantages of being born a male, and not having to go through what women do, seem to me to be quite enormous.

You don't have to read any of this stuff if you already know what they mean.

*An episiotomy is the surgical incision of the small area of skin and muscle located between the vagina and the anus, i.e., the perineum, to enlarge the vagina and so facilitate delivery during childbirth. I find it painful even writing these words.

*Dilation and curettage (D&C) refer to the dilation (widening/opening) of the cervix and surgical removal of part of the lining of the uterus and/or the contents of the uterus by scraping or scooping (curettage). It is the commonly used method for first trimester (13 weeks' pregnancy) miscarriage or abortion.

*A laparoscopy is an operation performed in the abdomen or pelvis using small incisions with the aid of a camera

*An abdominal hysterectomy is a surgical procedure that removes the uterus through an incision in the lower abdomen.

*Histology is the study of the microstructure of tissue.

*Choriocarcinoma is a fast-growing cancer that occurs in a woman's uterus (womb).

*Fibroids are non-cancerous tumours that grow in the uterus.

*The ureters are muscular tubes that propel urine from the kidneys to the urinary bladder.

*Peritoneum is the lining of the inner wall of the abdomen and cover of the abdominal organs

*Pre-eclampsia is a condition that affects some pregnant women, usually during the second half of pregnancy. Early signs are high blood pressure and protein in the urine. Although many cases are mild, the condition can lead to serious complications for both mother and baby if not monitored and treated.

*Retinitis is a disease that affects vision by damaging the retina – the light-sensing tissue at the back of the eye.

Dr D – THE YELLOW CARAVAN

The first few weeks as a junior house doctor are pretty frightening, and probably not just for the struggling fledgling doctor. The slightly more senior housemen and, above them, the registrars were approachable, but I tried to seek their help only when I felt completely out of my depth. In both my first and second appointments as a medical and then a surgical houseman, it took about two months before I felt the stirrings of some degree of confidence in my ability. I never knew what level of competence I was judged to have by the senior doctors, but when I had finished that first exhausting year and was now on the medical register the only comment I received, from a surgeon, was, "It's been fun having you Duncan, enjoy General Practice". No suggestion then that my departure from hospital medicine would deprive the service of a talented diagnostician or skilful surgeon who should be encouraged to change his decision to head for the unruliness of General Practice.

Without exception, the consultants I worked for were considerate, unlike their teaching hospital brethren who delighted in making you feel as cretinous and embarrassed as possible.

One of the BGH consultant physicians, Dr M, did employ a well-honed sardonic sense of humour when pointing out failings in the preliminary work of examining patients and organising the blood tests, X-rays and other investigations needed to reach a diagnosis, before his weekly ward round. Mostly, his jibes were accurate and fair criticism, but I bore a small grudge from a time when I had been unfairly judged to have misinterpreted a blood test result. This had made me look foolish in front of the patient, a man on whose investigation I had spent a lot of time and effort.

My chance for revenge presented itself not long before I was due to leave the medical wards. Dr M. phoned me late on a Sunday evening to say that he would like me to arrange the admission of an elderly lady, a patient of a notoriously inattentive local GP, who had suffered a stroke.

When I went to meet this slightly confused but delightful old lady on the ward, it was clear that she did have quite marked muscular weakness of the left side of her face. While there were absolutely no other findings to support the diagnosis of stroke, she did look slightly jaundiced.

"How long has your face felt a bit lopsided?" I asked

"Oh, I was born like that, Doctor"

Further questioning revealed that neither the infamous GP nor my consultant had ever been to see her. In fact, she was more surprised than confused at finding herself in a large ward of sleeping women, being questioned about her medical history. It transpired she had fallen outside her flat when putting out her milk bottle and had been spotted by a neighbour. They had phoned the GP, who then phoned his friend and golfing partner Dr M, who in turn phoned me and requested transport by ambulance. She wasn't sure why she was not at home watching the news on the 14" TV her sons had given her for Christmas.

But for me this was a heaven sent "Gotcha" moment and I wasted no time in investigating her mild jaundice with ferocious enthusiasm.

On the morning of the consultant's next ward round, I asked the staff nurse to move my old lady patient's bed so that hers would be the last case we presented to him.

"And who is this charming lady, Stewart?"

"This is the lady you admitted on Sunday night, sir"

"Ah, yes, the lady from Withdean. How are you getting on my dear?" he purred.

"Everyone's been very kind" she replied

"Has she started physiotherapy, Stewart?"

"No, sir, she hasn't."

"And why is that may I ask?" The tone of voice was now slightly more aggressive.

"Because she hasn't had a stroke sir, she was born with facial palsy."

His face displayed embarrassment and then resignation. After a few seconds I added "But she does have mild jaundice, which we have fully investigated, sir"

His facial expression changed to one of relief and slight amusement; he nodded a couple of times and, without waiting to hear the results of the extensive investigations I had arranged, he headed for the security of Sister's office with its waiting coffee and biscuits. I did my best to remain poker-faced.

Two weeks later, I was again the admitting doctor and received another late evening call from Dr M.

After the usual pleasantries he said he had another patient he would like admitted – an old lady who lived in a caravan with yellow painted walls and slept between yellow sheets, "...so I can't rule out jaundice with complete confidence."

Dr R – PAEDIATRICS – WHERE TO START?

Paediatrics, where to start? I guess the birth of my first baby would seem the natural place to begin. I was married to my first serious girlfriend. She went to Hove Grammar School for Girls, and I went to Hove Grammar School for boys. However, unlike most of the pupils, we both lived in the country, several miles outside of Hove and travelled in by train, which was where we met soon after my "O" levels. We courted through "A" levels. As previously mentioned, Heather went to a teacher's training college in London and the first 18 months of my studies were at Charing Cross Hospital Medical School, also in London. We married (four more years before my qualification) and my son, Ben, was born 18 months later at my own teaching hospital. I was doubly blessed in that this was the very first of many deliveries that I would witness, and that the pregnancy, delivery and subsequent outcome of our healthy baby was uncomplicated. We were young, and it all seemed so easy. Well, maybe a bit harder for Heather. The paediatric team took one peep at him and gave the thumbs-up.

On the seventh day, I drove my precious cargo down to Sussex to spend a week's break with my in-laws. Just on the outskirts of London I stopped at an accident. A young couple, early 20s at a guess, had been walking along the verge of the dual carriageway and a passing coach had somehow hit the girl. She was lying in the road and the boyfriend was sitting on the grass being comforted by some passers-by. I was the only medic on site, albeit only a medical student. The young lady was obviously dead, so I went over to her partner to give him the bad news. Well, I must have handled that as badly as anyone could have possibly done, because he jumped up and took a swipe at my face before anyone could restrain him. If he had connected, I sure would have known about it. The ambulance came, and we resumed our journey. Sadly, Heather, sitting in the back of the car with Ben on her lap, witnessed the whole horrific episode.

The day I qualified as a doctor, Heather had her first miscarriage, and I assisted at the D&C, as they were short-staffed!

For her second live birth, Heather returned to another of the Cross's teaching hospitals, The West London Hospital, for a "social induction" at 39 weeks' gestation. Early in her labour she was given intramuscular pethidine* for pain control only to deliver Matthew 30 minutes later. Matthew was hence, very "flat" and unresponsive at birth due to the influence of the pethidine passing through the placenta to him at a crucial moment. A colleague of mine in the year above me successfully, and extremely efficiently resuscitated our new-born. During my time at medical school, I had always viewed this chap as a bit of a nerd. Boy, did I change my mind! Heather, who I judged to be a natural sensible mum, struggled to bond with this little lad and felt that there was something wrong with him. A well-known Paediatric Consultant came along with his huge intimidating entourage and felt that a genetic investigation was warranted. Heather went back to Sussex after a few days, and I resumed work as a house surgeon at the New Charing Cross Hospital down the road. Two weeks later, I was summoned to the consultant's office to be informed that Matthew's genes showed up Trisomy 21, in other words, he was a '" Downs Syndrome" child. To use the derogatory terminology of the day, he was a "Mongol".

On the back of this awful news, I gave up my career in London and relocated to Sussex to be reunited with my family.

We went about trying to bring up our family and cope with a handicapped child. The boys were not vaccinated against whooping cough because of some worries that existed about the vaccine at the time so, through "sod's law" they both got it. Matthew was under six months and was quite poorly. He required admission to the Royal Alexandra Hospital for Children in Brighton. The nurses and doctors were fantastic at looking after our vulnerable little "Downs child". However, one nurse, who was the most involved with him, just didn't think that Matthew felt like a Downs when she was feeding him. This doubt went up the medical chain of command, to the Senior Paediatric Consultant, Dr Trevor Mann, who agreed. Another DNA sample was sent up, to Guy's Hospital this time, as they had a well-established genetic department under the leadership of Professor Polani. The result came back XYY, i.e., he had an extra Y (male) chromosome. At the time, there was a successful television crime series called The XYY Man, that my wife and I actually watched when we had the time. Based on some dodgy research in Scotland, it had been found that there was an increase of XYY males serving in high profile prisons, north of the border. This extra Y chromosome was thus nicknamed "the criminal chromosome". To quote a mate of mine over a few beers in the pub, "Blooming hell Rod, one minute you've got a music-loving 'dope', the next you're bringing up a psychopathic criminal."

We went to see Professor Polani, who reassured us that the findings were unfounded and that the main features that Matthew would be expected to show were that he would be taller than average and not too bright. Most of my "friends" thought that pretty much described me! Matthew survived, but it wasn't until we bumped into the alert nurse one day, that we realised how ill he had been and that we had nearly lost him on the ward.

As soon as I could, I made an appointment to see the Consultant Paediatrician back at the Cross, to see what he made of it all. He had been incredibly supportive of me when the diagnosis of Down syndrome came through, saying, "If there is absolutely anything I can do to help Rod, my door is always open." I was pretty miffed that my own teaching hospital had got it wrong but didn't have much chance to voice my frustration. "I think you're talking to the wrong department, Dr Brooks (no "Rod" now); you need to see the people in the genetic department." And that was that door firmly closed behind me.

I literally stormed down to the "incompetent" department to see the consultant in charge. The wind was completely taken out of my sails. "Hi Rod, isn't this great news." He showed me slides of Trisomy 21 and XYY, and I admit I could not tell the difference.

"Have you got time for a beer?" asked this very nice man; three pints later (it was only 11am in the morning), we shook hands and off I staggered back to the coast. This particular Paediatric Consultant wasn't very popular among us as medical students. Many years later, I was talking to a fairly new GP to Brighton, when his name popped up. "Oh yes, I was his SHO (Senior House Officer) for a year and was actually there when he collapsed on the ward round. I resuscitated him," she announced proudly.

"Why did you do that?" the words flew out of my mouth before I could stop them. "Everyone I tell that story to says the same thing," she muttered, rather deflated.

Two years later I was working at the local Children's Hospital (known locally as "the Alex") as part of my six-month paediatric training. The consultant was a truly lovely man, a Doctor Geoffrey Hatcher, who, prior to taking up a career in paediatrics, had worked as a GP in Devon. He was no "Ivory Tower" consultant. He knew exactly what GPs on the ground had to contend with. I explained to him that, for financial reasons I needed to do a lot of "moonlighting" on my evenings and weekends off and asked if he had any objections to that.

"You can do whatever you like when you are not here, but you are never to yawn on my ward round," was the somewhat "laissez faire" reply.

I had a fantastic six months and was still able to fit in some extra work. If I sent in a sick child in the middle of the night to the admitting doctor, I was able to switch the patient over to Dr Hatcher (and hence my own care the following morning). This meant I could describe in detail the whole social "picture" of where the sick child came from. This was so vital as it was important to know what the well child was going back to.

What I admired most of all about Dr Hatcher, was his lack of ego. I recall being on a crowded teaching ward round when he was explaining to an extremely young teenage mother what was wrong with her child. Very, very rarely for him, he pitched it at a level just above her comprehension, although she nodded with fake understanding. When the group moved on, I peeled off and spent a half-minute translating what he had said. Unbeknown to me, Dr Hatcher had spotted me and stopped the ward round to listen. This could have gone badly wrong for me until he remarked, "That's how you are supposed to do it." and moved on. I cannot think of any senior doctor that I have worked under who would have had that level of humility.

It was deeply satisfying to watch sick kids get better and be sent home with very grateful parents, as my wife and I had been two years earlier. However, there are inevitably times of great sadness. A four-year-old was sent in semi-comatose to me one evening. It turned out he had mumps encephalitis (I had generally seen mumps as a slight inconvenience to children); he took a turn for the worse and required ventilating. I cannot remember all the exact details, but after a few days of investigations, it was agreed with the parents that their child was brain dead and that there was no cure for this unfortunate lad. It was recommended that the ventilator should be turned off. The child would be expected to live unaided for less than an hour. A nurse was designated to sit with the dying boy and watch the ECG machine until it flat-lined, confirming death. The parents didn't want to stay for that, and so said their emotional goodbyes and left the nurse to her grim task.

I wasn't busy at the time so fetched a couple of cups of coffee and joined her. We admitted at the end that we had both been praying for a miracle and that the child would suddenly wake up fully recovered. Inevitably, our prayers were unanswered.

Six months later, I was back in the same ward looking at another child on a ventilator. I had just joined General Practice and been called out to a three-year-old boy with a fever. This happened after my Wednesday evening surgery; he had a middle ear infection, so I started him on the appropriate antibiotic and went home for my supper and an evening off.

Midway through my Thursday morning surgery the next day, I received a phone call from the father of the child with the earache. His son had deteriorated somewhat, despite starting on my recommended treatment, and they had phoned the duty doctor to see him. This "clever doctor" had been able to assess the situation on the phone and immediately sent for an ambulance. The bombshell was that the young lad was now in a coma and being ventilated at the Children's Hospital. I was pretty shaken by this news and found it very difficult to finish my surgery. When I eventually did, I shot off to the Alex to try to find out what had happened and what my role in it all was. As I knew the set-up in the hospital, and the staff knew me, I was able to access the notes. The admitting doctor had confirmed my diagnosis of Otitis Media* and continued the same treatment. It wasn't until 2am in the morning that the child had deteriorated and needed to be ventilated. It was all a bit of a mystery, but at least I felt exonerated. I went into the ward to have a look at the young boy. His parents were at the foot of the bed looking very glum. I must have looked shell-shocked because the father put his arm around my shoulder and said, "The Sister told us about what happened and your time working in the Children's Hospital. This isn't your fault Doctor, just rotten luck." Some people can be so magnanimous, even at the height of their own misery and I have never forgotten those few words – clearly.

Happily, the child fully recovered, and the rest is history. Ten years later, he came to the surgery, a six-foot teenager, complaining of earache again. I couldn't see much down either ear and he didn't have a fever, so I recommended paracetamol and sent him on his way. As he was leaving, he popped his head around the door and challenged me, "I won't need ventilating then Doc?"

"Get out of here." I retorted, as I suffered a horrible flashback!

Heather, my wife, had cleared off to Devon on an art course and I was "looking after" my kids in one of the playgrounds one day, when Ben fell off a swing and cut his knee. It required stitches so off we went to the Accident and Emergency Department of The Royal Sussex County Hospital. I was in the middle of a six-month stint there, so was able to get one of my colleagues to sew him up without having to wait too long. The following weekend, Ben fell off the same swing and cut his other knee. I knew that if you turned up at the local Casualty with your child, who had suffered two injuries in a short space of time, the social workers would be alerted and would visit the home unannounced to assess our parental skills. Well, I wasn't having that, so I sneaked him into Casualty and sewed up his other knee myself, "forgetting" to record the visit.

One year later, I was enjoying my six months in Paediatrics at the Royal Alexandra Children's Hospital in Brighton. It was 7pm and I had just started my evening "on call" shift when my wife rang me to inform me that Matthew, aged two and half, had stuck a pea up his nose and she couldn't get it out. I was a paediatrician, albeit very junior, so I knew what I was doing. My wife brought him up to the hospital and with the help of the night sister acquired a pair of very slim surgical forceps. We were able to use them to remove the little green vegetable without any lasting damage to my son's nostril. Off they went back home. An hour later, my wife rang to say that Matthew had sneezed, and another pea had come flying out of his nose. I hadn't thought to have a look up his other nostril!

Another two years later, I had just started my first week in General Practice. On my first half-day, we decided to celebrate as a family by going out for a bite to eat in one of the local restaurants. As we were leaving the house, Ben fell off the garden wall and fractured his left wrist. We all had lunch that day out of the food and drinks dispensing machine in Casualty!

I learnt to swim in a rock pool on a beach in Cornwall when I was five years old. By the time I was ten, I fancied myself as a half decent swimmer. My specialty was to see how far I could swim underwater in my local swimming pool. I can remember well that extraordinary feeling of my lungs on the verge of bursting as I surfaced gasping for air. I thought at the time (a bit morbidly for a ten-year-old) that this would be an impossible way to commit suicide and that, if ever felt a need for self-destruction at a future date, I would have to think of a different modus operandi. (I probably used the word "method" though.)

All these thoughts were flashing through my subconscious when I was confronted with a mum and dad with their child in the Paediatric Outpatient's Department of the Alex. I had just started a six-month posting and was standing in for the Senior Registrar, who had been called away on some emergency. This was a little outside my comfort zone to say the least, but I had the back-up of my consultant in the examination room next door. The child in question was a pretty little girl of around eight years old.

Her mum said that she was perfectly well physically and emotionally and that they had experienced very few problems with her upbringing so far. She was an only child as they had only wanted to have one. The reason for the child's referral was that, over the last six months, the little girl (we will call her Mary) had taken to holding her breath. This had initially been for a few seconds once or twice a week, but now had increased to 30-second periods, up to four times a day. The parents were terrified that their daughter was going to die. I asked the standard background questions and examined the child who appeared absolutely normal. Having read about "breath holding attacks in the young" in the run up to my finals, I was pretty confident that this was a benign, self-limiting condition, one that all children grow out of it without coming to any harm. The best way forward was probably to ignore it when she held her breath. It was important to stay calm and not transfer any alarm over to the child. I thought, that shouldn't be too difficult, should it?

I had just delivered my mini lecture on good parenting when this child decided to hold her breath in front of me. This appeared to last for at least 10 minutes, before there was any indication of it ending. (Clearly it wasn't 10 minutes as my record was only a minute and twenty seconds, but it felt like it.)

"Stay calm and ignore her," I reassured her parents. However, it got to a point where I was beginning to think that this blooming child was going to expire in front of me just to prove me wrong. The palms of my hands were quite moist as I was reaching for the emergency phone when Mary had the decency to exhale. "There, I told you so," I squeezed out of my contracted voice box. "No harm done." But I would like you all to see my consultant before you go." With some effort, I managed to smile at the child. Did I imagine it, or did she give me a little wink before the family left my room?

---

*Pethidine is a strong analgesic traditionally used to help with the pain associated with childbirth.

*An ivory tower is a state of privileged seclusion or a separation from the facts and practicalities of the real world. With reference to a consultant, it usually meant he was an utter prat!

*Otitis Media is a middle-ear infection. The final diagnosis was a viral encephalitis causing swelling of the brain, which responded to treatment

Dr D – BAPTISM OF FIRE

One evening halfway through my third, obstetric hospital job, my wife Sue and I went for a drink at The Wick Inn on Palmeira Square in Hove. Sitting in one corner wearing a Guy's scarf was Martin Garvey, who I recognised from my student days but had never met. We were soon in conversation; he mentioned that he needed a partner because the GP he had joined only a couple of years earlier was unwell and was retiring soon. I said that I would be interested once I had completed a paediatric house job, which would complete what I saw as an appropriate two years of postgraduate experience before starting a career in General Practice.

"Don't worry about that," boomed Martin, "I can teach you paediatrics in a fortnight" And so it was that two pints later, it was agreed that we would become partners.

Not having completed a GP training course, if indeed there was such a thing in Brighton in 1969, my move into General Practice involved registering with the Executive Council in Lewes and accepting a contract that committed me to being continually responsible for all patients registered with me for 365 days a year. I also had to upgrade my professional indemnity insurance and to sign the practice accountancy agreement. This in turn necessitated convening a meeting with Martin and the outgoing partner, which took place in the practice accountant's office.

Local gossip had reached me, which suggested that far from his being forced, as he claimed, to retire on grounds of ill health, he was on the point of being struck off the medical register for overprescribing drugs with addictive potential and inappropriate relationships.

What was undoubtedly true was that he had a reputation for what might be called a minimalist approach to the job. Unsuspecting patients were impressed by his ability '"to diagnose anything over the phone". However, his presence on the junior hospital doctors' unofficial blacklist of GPs who tried to admit patients they had not examined was firmly established.

He drove a large American car, which he parked with the engine running while he ran in and out of home visits. I felt sure I had never met him, certainly not at any GP educational event held in the Postgraduate Centre.

The meeting was farcical. He was below average height with a marked divergent squint like Marty Feldman. He was well dressed, and he spoke with a delightful Irish brogue. After expressing his sadness at having to abandon his patients, he said that I had an excellent reputation, and he was relieved to be leaving his practice in such good hands!

I said how sorry I was to hear he was ill. Slowly and silently, with a very sombre expression on his face he withdrew an ECG tracing from his top pocket. The recording showed the changes associated with severe coronary artery disease, which would indeed have been alarming for him, had it been his.

He disappeared to work in central London with a couple of medical fraudsters, the Harris brothers, who ran a weight loss clinic in central London. This was the era when girls were desperate to be as thin as Twiggy and to be able to squeeze into Mary Quant's creations. At lunchtime, a queue would form as they waited for the magic weight reducing injection. This was simply a dose of a diuretic, which made them pass a couple of pints of urine, but the weight returned to its previous level the following day.

I had reason to call one of these brothers a couple of years later, when the wife of a well-known London publican, who had a weekend flat in Brighton, asked me to visit her husband, a big tough-looking man, who had lost a lot of weight.

I arrived to find him sitting in an armchair, weeping. I took a careful history, examined him thoroughly and found no evidence of physical disease. At this point, he admitted something he had not told his much younger and very beautiful wife.

Dr Harris had given him some pills to get his weight down; he fished out two bottles of pills resembling nothing I had ever seen before. One contained large bright turquoise tablets and the others were a vivid purple colour. The labels gave no clue as to their content, so I phoned the prescriber, who said they contained "a bit of thyroid hormone and some Amphetamine." The doses of both were dangerously high.

I flushed them all down the loo and assured him he would feel normal within a week. At this point, his wife promised she would still love him even if he did put back a few pounds.

My initial assessment of the GP I was replacing was that he was simply a lazy and incompetent rogue. However, I developed a serious dislike of him when Martin and I discovered a year later that his failure to pay his share of the practice tax bill meant that he and I were forced to pay substantial sums for which we should not have been liable. Had I ever met him again he might have had more to worry about than a squint.

Dr R – POTATO PAUL

My year as a trainee was spent happily in the largest practice in the area. My trainer, Dr Paul, was very critical of my dress code; casual cords and an open neck shirt (always clean). By contrast, Dr Paul always turned up in a three-piece double-breasted suit with waistcoat and military tie. There was also the odd reference to the length of my hair. After a bit of a row, I pointed out that I did not own a double-breasted suit and that if I had done, I would not wear one to examine screaming babies with diarrhoea and vomiting. He seemed to get the message and turned up the next day in a brand-new sparkling combat outfit, looking even more inappropriate. I asked him for the name of his tailor, but I think he thought I was being sarcastic.

Not long after this particularly trying time, the police rang the surgery to try to locate the duty doctor – (this was before mobile phones). It was around 2pm and everyone was out visiting patients except my trainer, who was on his half day. This he spent cultivating potatoes in the garden at the back of the practice: not my choice of half-day recreation! According to the police, one of the partner's patients had gone "bonkers" (their term of phrase) and needed sectioning*. I was suitably impressed to learn that "Potato Paul" responded and visited the patient who was diagnosed as a *paranoid schizophrenic, out of control and needed emergency admission to the psychiatric hospital." A month later, the discharge letter landed on my desk. It read, and I quote, "The patient on arrival was clearly psychotic, describing the attending doctor as having been dressed in a filthy jumper, shorts, muddy wellington boots and a straw hat." Although he quickly settled into hospital, his hallucinations regarding his GP never changed, despite quite large doses of anti-psychotic medication!

*In most cases when people are treated in hospital or another mental health facility, they have agreed or volunteered to be there. You may be referred to as a voluntary, albeit reluctant, patient. But there are cases when a person can be detained, also known as sectioned, under the Mental Health Act (1983) and treated without their agreement. People detained under this particular piece of legislation need urgent treatment for a mental disorder and are at risk of harm to themselves or others – the latter would seem to describe many of the colleagues I trained with at medical school.

*Paranoid schizophrenia is a major psychotic disorder whose symptoms include delusions, hallucinations, and disorganised thinking among others. This is not a rare illness and affects 20 million people worldwide and very very few harm others, as some tabloid papers would have it.

Dr D – LOCUM TENENS

For single-handed GPs and small practices, finding a locum for night, weekend or holiday cover was often a major and stressful task for the doctor, and an unpredictable experience for the locum. My immediate superior as a House Surgeon was a Junior Surgical Registrar called Simon who became a very competent and probably now a very rich plastic surgeon, but in these early impecunious days, as he was married with two children, he decided to do a GP locum and forego a two-week holiday between surgical appointments. He was interviewed for the job by the eccentric Irish senior partner, who he was temporarily replacing and was introduced to the Scottish junior partner and to Margaret the practice manager, the only other staff member. This lady, a legend in the area, ran the practice like a personal fiefdom, was fiercely protective of "her doctors" and was never known to have been outmanoeuvred by any patient, however devious. She controlled patient access to the doctors by sitting in the waiting room, questioning the need for a consultation, and chucking out anyone she decided was a timewaster. She would also lock and unlock the front door at precisely the advertised opening hours. When not at work, she could usually be found in the pub next door.

Simon, who knew nothing about General Practice, coped well

with the varied and unfamiliar problems that came through the door but was glad to have finished the Friday morning surgery and to be able to enjoy the prospect of a restful weekend and a chance to complete his research paper.

Margaret came in, as she did every morning, with coffee in an elegant porcelain cup and saucer, and a plate of biscuits. "I've brought you the journals, Doctor." She said as she placed a small pile of them on the floor next to the desk. When Simon had finished writing a couple of referral letters and entering notes in a few sets of patient notes, he reached down for the journals and was intrigued to find himself holding the latest copies of Opera, Boxing Weekly and Playboy.

Some years later, after it had been agreed that GPs should be relieved of the onerous task of covering out-of-hours care, a GP cooperative was set up, BrightDoc, which at first was manned entirely by local GPs. It provided 24-hour cover for the whole city. A couple of cars with drivers made visiting a lot simpler but most patients were seen at the clinic in the outpatient building. During a busy Saturday afternoon session, a middle-aged man came in with an extremely fat girl, his daughter Tracey, who was the patient. I estimated that she was at least 10 stone overweight.

"What can I do for you, Tracey?" I asked as soon as they were seated. She stared at the floor.

"She's got a rash."

"And how long have you had this, Tracey?"

"'About free days" volunteered the father.

"Does it itch, Tracey?" She continued to find the flooring a source of fascination.

"Yeah," said the father. Tracey was clearly never going to be allowed to speak unless separated from her father, so I suggested she cross the room and lie on the couch, which reacted noisily to the weight it was now having to support.

On examination, she had quite an extensive allergic rash for which there could be any one of dozens of possible causes. I ploughed through the list of antibiotics, painkillers and other medications, with her father continuing to do all the talking. No, she hadn't had anything like this before, she had no pets, no new house plants no change of washing powder and no cosmetics – I could see that for myself.

There was an air of expectancy that I would identify the cause, but I was running out of possible culprits. But then I had a flash of inspiration.

"This is the time of year when the fresh summer fruits appear – could you be allergic to strawberries or raspberries or even tomatoes?"

Her father, who had clearly begun to enjoy the prospect of my diagnostic failure and consequent embarrassment, clutched the large gold crucifix resting on his sleeveless vest and proclaimed proudly "She don't eat nuffin like that, doc." And I believed him.

Dr R – WHAT'S YOUR TIPPLE?

It was 1974 and I had just bought my very first house in Kemptown. I was almost through the Brighton GP Vocational Training Scheme and was very busy and very hard up. The children were still too young for Heather to resume her career in teaching. I grabbed as much extra work as I could and was fortunate enough to have a regular slot on my half day away from the Accident and Emergency department where I was working at the time. This source of regular income came from acting as the locum to a single-handed female GP in North Brighton. She was a bit of a character to say the least, but I grew very fond of her. The practice was run from a couple of rooms in her house. She would employ her regular receptionist to look after me while she put her feet up in her living room. She was approaching retirement age and I thought, good luck to her, as I could hear her giggling at her favourite TV programme in the background. I think she had done her bit for the NHS for over forty years. Her sense of timing was absolutely perfect because she seemed to sense when I was coming near to the end of my surgery. There would be a tap on the door to her living room behind me, and she would slip me a huge, most welcome, gin and tonic, saying; "I thought you'd like a cold lemonade to keep you going." I thought this was a very forward way of thinking but was never successful in getting my partners in General Practice (when I finally got there), to accept this form of refreshment. Perhaps I should have opted to go single-handed and have a bottle of gin on my desk, at all times! One particular evening near Christmas, I was gifted an extra-large glass of sustenance. Before I could pack up for home, I desperately needed a pee. The bathroom was located up a particularly steep set of stairs; in my jolly state, I reckoned that there were about 40 steps, there and back. The combination of relieving a full bladder and being slightly inebriated was making me feel quite heady. I missed the last step on my descent and seemed to fall in slow motion. On the way to the surgery, I had been desperately trying to remember the last book that I had read. Strangely, it suddenly came to me during my short aerial flight. "Of course, it was John Buchan's The Thirty-Nine Steps, and I've just missed the last one!" My ankle swelled up literally as I watched it. As I was unable to drive, I was carted off to Casualty by ambulance. I was a valued colleague working in the same department, so I was seen four hours' later having been put bottom of the waiting list. Young drunk men who had fallen over and injured themselves were treated, quite rightly in my view up until then, with a certain lack of sympathy.

My little white lie, complaining that I had been attacked, didn't cut any ice either. To my disappointment, I hadn't fractured my ankle and was expected in the department the next day as usual. My dream of having the next six weeks off work, on full pay, while the bones slowly repaired, were shattered.

Dr D – MY FIRST PRIVATE PATIENT

I first ventured into General Practice by applying to be a locum for a doctor who lived above his surgery in West Hove. I remember him being tall, overweight, moustachioed, kindly, and clearly concerned about his patients. He was very upset about a recent event involving a neighbour whose pregnant wife had gone into hospital, suffered a miscarriage and then died in hospital. On the same day, their three-year-old son had wandered out through their unsecured front door and into the road. There, he had been hit by a lorry and killed instantly, leaving this poor man devastated by the sudden loss of his whole family. Anyone would have found this story distressing, but I later learned that the doctor and his wife had also lost two children: a daughter who had died from asthma and a son from leukaemia.

Another doctor, known as Fizz, who had worked in this practice, was looking after her sick mother and could not work full-time so we did a job share. I was very aware of being entirely inexperienced in General Practice and was very grateful for the support she generously offered. Knowing how ignorant I was and not being too arrogant, I became a slow but very thorough novice. I took long histories and examined absolutely everyone on the basis that we can't all be skilled, but we can be thorough. I was relieved to find that I really did enjoy this first taste of my chosen career and, even in just two weeks, I learned a lot.

I was on call over the first weekend of the locum and made several home visits, including one on the Sunday morning to a 21-year-old man with abdominal pain and vomiting, who was staying with his aunt and uncle in Mile Oak, West Hove. His looking pretty rough, not a strictly medical description, was explained by it having been his birthday the day before. Among other things, during the evening celebration, he had consumed a large vindaloo curry and at least eight pints of lager. I couldn't find anything seriously wrong with him, so I gave him an injection to stop the vomiting and reassured them all that he would be better soon.

"Thank you for coming out on a Sunday, Doctor; you must treat this as a private visit."

I had no idea what the fee should be and was embarrassed by the need to charge any fee for my services so I deferred the problem by saying I would see him again later in the day. In fact, I saw him three more times, twice completely unnecessarily, before I had the courage to suggest that "£5 would be fine."

"That doesn't seem much," said his mum, and handed me a tenner.

Four years later, I found myself working full-time in an almost entirely private practice and continued to see patients, mainly on a private basis, until I retired. This was not an active choice, and it was neither ideological nor part of a scheme to get rich – I simply found the conditions very agreeable. My partner and I worked long hours and did a lot of "out of hours" work but were under less pressure and less control than our NHS colleagues and we enjoyed the luxury of spending more time with our patients. My small NHS list was hardly typical, containing 450 Roedean schoolgirls, doctors and their families and a few patients rejected or ejected by other local practices and allocated to me by what was called The Executive Council in those days (it has now become the CCG or Clinical Commissioning Group).

Dr R – TIME TO GO

The period from doing my "A levels" at Grammar School to my first day in General Practice lasted about 10 years, give or take. I replaced the senior partner in a practice of four in central Brighton. In those days, I had to undergo a six-month trial to check if we were all compatible and that it was all going to work. General Practice is potentially a long marriage. I became a junior partner on two-thirds salary before gaining full parity in another two and half years. My workload in those early days was very light compared with my Vocational Training, which had been mostly based in hospitals as a junior "dogsbody" doctor working in various specialties.

My first day in General Practice was largely uneventful, so much so that I can only remember the evening when the night cleaner came in especially early to introduce himself to me. He had recently moved to the area but had worked as a cleaner in a similar practice somewhere along the south coast. I was quite flattered by his effort, but it turned out that a few weeks previously he had found the senior partner, who was coming up for retirement, "dead" on the examination couch. Having recently been trained in cardiac resuscitation, he was eager to have a go. He had the fright of his life when the elderly doctor whispered, "Oh, it's Jim, I must have fallen asleep." The cleaner clearly didn't want a repeat of this experience. I think I was able to reassure him but stopped short of promising. Apparently, the same partner had been disturbed peeing in his surgery sink by one of the junior female receptionists bringing him a cup of tea. Apparently, the young lady had since left to pursue her career elsewhere. It was probably the right time for the doctor to retire. I, at least, always make sure I lock the door and run the taps in order to avoid offence.

Dr D – THE UNFORGETTABLE VERA

I had been working in my new practice for no more than a week when the first memorable event occurred. To picture the scene, we were housed in a small prefab building in a corner of a petrol station forecourt. There was only one entrance, which was to the waiting area and in one corner of that quite modest area sat our rather eccentrically dressed receptionist who, I always suspected, must belong to some joyless, fundamental "low" church. There were two internal doors, one leading to a toilet and one to the doctor's room with its small separate examination room. This was long before most practices had any form of appointment system; on most mornings, there would be 30 or 40 patients waiting to be seen, many of them only wanting a sick note. However, everyone who arrived before the door was locked at 11am was seen before I left to do home visits. It was not unusual to see 50 people in a morning surgery and then do six or eight home visits before an afternoon session starting at 4pm, and then a few more visits. I rarely got home before 7 o'clock.

The phone on my desk rang, an event usually restricted to urgent calls, and I heard the receptionist's shrill voice say, "Vera's out."

"Who is Vera?" I asked, not unreasonably.

"You haven't met her but hurry up this is urgent."

"What's the problem, do I need my bag?"

"No, just get over the road as fast as you can."

So, I did as I was told, struggling into my jacket while dodging the traffic as I ran across the Lewes Rd.

The person I assumed to be in need of my help, Vera, was standing 20 yards up Gladstone Road, wearing sensible brown shoes, carrying a matching handbag, and nothing else. The distracted look on her face changed, briefly displaying some sign of interest, when I introduced myself. I suggested she might like me to take her home; before I could offer her the use of my jacket, she turned to go up the road. With me holding her by the arm, we walked slowly and in silence up the deserted road passing ever-higher numbers on the front doors and the twitching net curtains in the windows of the modest terraced houses. We had almost reached the top when Vera spoke for the first time, in a slightly triumphant tone.

"We live at number 6. Mother's looking forward to meeting you."

We turned around and sedately walked back down the entire length of the road until we reached the open door of number 6. Her mother, a wizened old lady with nicotine-stained hair and fingers, greeted me warmly, offered me tea and thanked me for returning her daughter.

"She's not as cooperative with everyone, Doctor. I think she must like you." I didn't stay for the tea.

Dr R – FAUX PAS

As a medical student, I fell into many verbal traps.

I asked a poorly controlled epileptic if he was feeling "fit" today.

I invited an above the knee amputee if he would "hop" up onto his bed so that I could examine him.

There have been countless other examples.

For instance, John, the stepfather of my wife, Louise, died at the age of 87. Louise's son Carl flew back from the United States for the cremation. The undertaker opened the mortuary the night before, so that Carl could say goodbye privately. I was struck how "well" John looked lying in his coffin with his shock of wiry white hair. "Gosh," I said to the undertaker, trying to make small talk. "What an amazing head of hair John has! You would die for that wouldn't you!" The undertaker diplomatically smiled and nodded.

New patients to the practice were formally registered by one of the doctors. This involved quite a lot of form filling, and I must admit it wasn't the most exciting part of my job, but unfortunately a necessary evil. Sometimes, the receptionists would accidently (or was it on purpose?) give me a new registration appointment in the middle of a Monday morning surgery. This was usually our busiest time, after the weekend. In walked a smartly dressed young man about the same age as me, which was 35 years old at the time. Routine background questions revealed that he was a gay man who had recently split up with his boyfriend after a five-year monogamous relationship. This had happened about three months earlier, and he was still feeling a little raw emotionally. He became quite tearful as he told me his story.

This registration was taking a bit longer than I had anticipated and I was running very late in the surgery. In an attempt to make my new vulnerable patient feel at ease with me, I leant over, put a gentle hand on his forearm and said, "I hate these blooming forms. Don't let's bugger around in here, let's go downstairs and do it." I am not quite sure that had the desired effect, as he seemed to be a little startled. However, he soon settled down as I was still smiling encouragingly at him. He just said, "Yes, Doctor, I would like that." The thing is, I rarely use the word "bugger": plenty of other expletives, but not that one!

Dr D – CEREMONIAL CONFUSION

I met Barry at my first Saturday morning surgery in my first practice in 1969. I had become his new GP and I suspect he came simply to make sure that I emitted no whiff of antisemitism as I cannot recall our talking about his health. However, I can recall in detail the shaggy dog story he told me about a second-hand car dealer who buys an elephant to publicise his business. As the absurd story progressed, Barry, a consummate storyteller with a great sense of the ridiculous, was encouraged by my obvious enjoyment, to invent ever more insane details. After about five minutes, I was crying with laughter, and lying on the floor barely able to breathe. We became friends.

Ten years later, Barry's heavy smoking caught up with him and although he had his lung tumour removed, the disease was not eradicated and his last year was tough for him, his family and, to a lesser extent, for me.

My father had died from stomach cancer in 1970, after a year-long illness in which he suffered relentless weight loss, nausea, and abdominal pain. He had a lifelong history of depression and my mother, brother and I decided, quite wrongly but with good intent, not to inform him of his real diagnosis, a decision that still haunts me.

I suspect he may have known the true situation but accepted

our elaborate deception as a way of protecting us from having to cope with his emotions.

This chastening experience equipped me to be able to talk openly to Barry about all aspects of his illness and the inevitability of his dying from it, and we spent many hours together, some punctuated by laughter and some by tears.

His wife, Esther, was also a friend first and patient second. She was a handsome woman, who was always beautifully dressed and also possessed of a fine sense of humour. Some years after her husband's death, she began an affair with a well-known political journalist. He came down to Brighton once or twice a month for lunch and they spoke every day on the phone.

"What do you give him to eat?" asked her daughter.

"Smoked salmon sandwiches."

"Is that all?"

"Yes, he doesn't come here for the food, darling – and sandwiches are the best things to eat in bed!"

I met the new lover a couple of times at the parties she held. On one occasion, knowing that he had been moved to a "redtop" newspaper, something he considered a demotion, I asked about the job.

"Oh, I suppose it's alright," he sighed. "I'm now the political editor. They pay me well but it's a bit like being the charcuterie correspondent for The Jewish Chronicle."

At the start of one of their evening phone calls, he asked what Esther had been doing, and was reminded that this was the Jewish New Year, and despite not being a religious person, she had made her annual visit to the synagogue.

"And what goes on there?" he asked.

"Well," she said, "it's a special service a bit like your Christmas." She went on to describe the food involved, the relevant prayers and music, and the history-laden address given by the Rabbi after he had taken The Torah and the ram's horn trumpet from their cases.

Our journalist friend was clearly interested in the details of the ceremony.

"What happens next?"

"The Rabbi reads the appropriate passages from the Torah and then he blows the Shofar."

"Did you say he blows the chauffeur? My God, you Jews know how to treat your staff."

At one time, my practice included three people, a woman and two men, who all had concentration camp numbers tattooed on their forearms. I feel that this visible evidence of the horrendous suffering the Jews had experienced, both over their long history, in Egypt for instance, and at the hands of the Fascist dictators who were still alive when I was born, somehow catalysed a change in my attitude from the sort of casual antisemitism I had grown up with to a feeling of protective affection.

Dr R – A VERY FORTUNATE MAN

Bernard and Connie lived next door to me in Kemptown, handy for the Royal Sussex County Hospital, 200 yards away, and opposite the private secondary school, Brighton College. The sea was only a three-minute walk to the south. The couple lived over their business, a small shop that appeared to sell every tiny incidental as well as doubling up as a "Tuck Shop" for the boys and girls across the road. Bernard developed shingles and a cough. A chest X-ray showed both lungs to be full of incurable cancer. A chest surgeon in Bevendean Chest Hospital in Brighton declared him terminal.

He wasn't a patient of mine as I was still working in the Vocational Training Scheme. However, the registered GP allowed me to be involved in his terminal care. He became very confused in the hospital and would try to break free every evening. As soon as we got him home and back in his own bed, he settled down to spend his last days with his family. All the family were devoutly Catholic, and their combined love and faith was very moving to be around. I gave Bernard the necessary amounts of morphine derivatives, some oral, others to be administered intramuscularly as and when he needed it to keep him comfortable. Every evening, the whole family, including the young grandchildren and myself, would gather around the bed, whether Bernard was asleep or not.

We would chat quite naturally in his presence. Most mornings and afternoons, I was able to pop in as I only lived 10 yards away. After two weeks, Bernard started to deteriorate quite significantly and his wife called a family meeting (excluding the youngsters this time), to ask me if there was anything that could be done to help her husband through this difficult period. I reassured them that I could give the appropriate treatment to reduce his increasing discomfort and restlessness. After we had all agreed to this pathway forward, I popped upstairs to give Bernard an appropriate injection. As I was preparing his skin, he put a gentle hand on my wrist and whispered, "I'm not quite ready yet, Rod."

"OK, Bernard, I quite understand," I said as I replaced the sheath on the needle. I reported back downstairs and Bernard, with little back-up from me, lived for a further three days and then succumbed. I was very privileged to be there for the 30 minutes leading up to his ultimate death. All the family, including the grandchildren, witnessed the calm and dignified passing of a very well-loved man. This all happened during the unusually hot summer of 1976, but Connie managed to keep him home while awaiting the funeral. I would visit Connie at least twice a day during this time and this was always spent upstairs with Bernard. The children and grandchildren visited their dead grandfather right up to his funeral. The whole process seemed so normal and natural. No visiting the dead at the undertakers, and no dying in hospital. I count Bernard as one of the most fortunate men that I have ever met. The family's impact on me as a young doctor was immense. Connie went to live in Europe with her other daughter and was joined later by her sister. I still exchange Christmas cards with her daughter in Brighton and did the same with Connie herself up until she died, a few years ago. If there is a heaven, then that is where Bernard and Connie are now, sharing a joke.

Dr D – FLIES

My male friends never seem to fully accept my assertion that lust is the last emotion a male doctor experiences when examining women patients' bodies. For example, taking a cervical smear, which is obviously not a procedure much enjoyed by the patient either, is far more likely to cause the doctor anxiety than sexual stimulation. Will he be able to see the cervix and then succeed in taking a valid specimen and not have to do it all again?

I'm not suggesting that a medical qualification somehow robs you of libido, or the inability to appreciate the female form, it's just that I always felt perfectly comfortable about examining women.

One couple I looked after had made a lot of money quite quickly by setting up a novel retailing system for selling women's tights, which were becoming much more varied and more popular in the 70s. Their choice of holiday was to fly out to Hollywood in February, book into a smart hotel and mingle with the wannabes of the film industry. Soon after returning from one of these jaunts, Mrs D kept her appointment for a routine smear test. She was a very good-looking woman, made even more attractive by a deep suntan. Without stopping to sit down, she strode through my consulting room towards the examination room hoisting her cheesecloth dress over her head on the way and then lay down on the examination couch, completely naked.

All the surgical instruments we used in those days were made of stainless steel. They had to be washed and put through the steam sterilizer before being reused. While I assembled what I needed to take a cervical smear, she chatted away about her trip and how they had met Ed "Kookie" Byrnes, who had starred in some long-forgotten sitcom.

The woman who cleaned our rooms was fairly efficient but not overzealous and Mrs D, staring up at the ceiling, noticed that the plastic cover over the strip light was full of the dead bodies of an assortment of flying insects.

"Oh Duncan," said this fastidious woman with a husky voice," I would love to get at those 'flies' of yours."

"Mrs D," I replied in the sternest voice I could muster. "The General Medical Council has thousands of reports containing the details of lewd suggestions made to doctors by sex-obsessed women like you!"

Even the darkest tan could not have hidden the ensuing blush, which seemed to start well below her navel. Only when she finally stopped giggling did we manage to fulfil the original purpose of her visit.

She did get her own back a few years later, at a party where many of the guests were also my patients. As soon as we reached the party room, she walked straight up to me gave me an unexpectedly long and full-on kiss. She then turned to my wife and told her, "I wouldn't go with him dear if I was you, he'll charge you £30 to take your clothes off, like the rest of us!"

Dr R – A SECOND OPINION

We often took the opportunity to seek each other's advice in the practice if possible. It felt much more like a group-integrated surgery working this way. A good example of this policy was when, on one bright and sunny afternoon, in sashayed a bright young sunny airhostess, (now called "cabin crew"). "What brings you in today?" I asked. "I've got a small spot that has appeared on the inside of my upper thigh, Doctor" she replied shyly. I had a peep, but it was difficult to see without getting on my knees and I wasn't about to do that. A better plan was for her to stand on a chair, so I could view the lesion at eye level while still sitting in the comfort of my own chair. Her little "worry" appeared to be an ordinary benign mole that I suspected had been there a long time. However, just to make sure I decided on a second opinion. Only one of my partners was available, so I rang him. "I have a Virgin Air Hostess with me who is worried about what looks like a little mole on the inside of her upper thigh. If you have a moment I wonder if you could pop up?" It would seem that he had hung up on me as there was no answer, but what the patient and I could hear was the thudding of someone running full pelt up the surgery stairs and bursting into my room without knocking. I had a good view of my partner through the inverted 'V' of the young lady's legs, still balancing on my chair. "Gosh, that didn't take long," exclaimed the rather startled woman. I began to "lose it", so I had to excuse myself to allow the delighted doctor to complete the consultation. I was unable to continue my surgery until the patient had left the premises and my colleague had returned to his room. I spent a few minutes collecting myself and reflecting on how I could have managed the consultation differently. I concluded that it had gone pretty well. Anyway, I didn't hear any complaints, even from the doctor whose workload I had temporarily increased.

Dr D – ROEDEAN CHARM

One of the consultants I worked for at Brighton General Hospital was Mrs Connie Beynon, a consultant obstetrician and gynaecologist, who had also run her husband's General Practice while he was away in the RAMC (Royal Army Medical Corp) during the war. She was a pretty formidable woman, quite demanding but very fair. Not long after I started in GP, she phoned me and asked if I could act as her locum as Medical Officer at Roedean School while she and her husband went on holiday. I knew that the other Medical Officer, a retired rheumatologist, was quite elderly and that I was possibly being vetted to see if I was a suitable replacement.

In those days the Sanatorium, a large Victorian building, with about a dozen beds and a large consulting room, was at the east end of the campus, downwind of the main school buildings, which housed the classrooms, dining room, offices and the four residential houses, unimaginatively named 1 to 4. There was a separate Junior House, and no day pupils. It was a single-sex school with wonderful facilities for sports and arts. I was immediately impressed by the good care the staff took of their charges. The matron was a delightful and very competent woman, a single mother, but quite easily outmanoeuvred by girls trying to find medical reasons for avoiding events they disliked. The nurse was much savvier and could sniff out a malingerer in seconds. I think they enjoyed my working with them, and I made no significant errors either medically or of protocol, so when I was asked to see the headmaster at the end of my two-week stint, I felt I stood a good chance of this becoming a permanent arrangement if there was indeed about to be a vacancy.

John Hunt was a tall, gentle, erudite man with exquisitely good manners. After asking if I had enjoyed my time at the school and thanking me for helping out, he asked if doing the work had been a difficult addition to my workload, whether my partner had been put to any inconvenience and whether I was married. I reassured him there were no problems. Then he asked my age. I told him I was 25.

"For God's sake, tell them you're 30," he said, "you're only five years older than the oldest girl!"

I was officially appointed, given an honorarium, which was useful, and took up my post at the start of the Autumn Term. The housemistresses and the teaching staff I encountered were all very kind and supportive. However, for the girls, especially the older ones, I was a sitting target for their charm offensives. I must have coped reasonably well because just before the school emptied for the Christmas holiday a very pretty 16-year-old and her friend insisted on seeing me, together, at the end of my morning surgery.

"Dr Stewart," she said blushing "we have an award for you."

I thanked them and said that this was a very pleasant Christmas present.

"Yes" she said, "You have been elected Roedean's best-dressed man."

Given that apart from the headmaster, the bursar, and the head of the Physics department, I hadn't come across any other males this didn't sound like a great honour, but I thanked them again and felt quite pleased, until her friend added

" Yes, in the end it was between you and the head groundsman."

I worked at the school and thoroughly enjoyed the work for the next 35 years.

Dr R – TAKING THE PISS

While still working at the Royal Sussex County Hospital in Brighton as a Junior Hospital Doctor, in the Accident and Emergency Department, I noticed an advert for a weekly medical session at the local bread factory, Acres the Bakers. The premises dominated the hill overlooking Woodingdean, a suburb of Brighton. If the wind were in a favourable direction, the lucky population would be greeted in the early hours with a rather wonderful, sweet aroma of thousands of loaves of bread slowly baking in the factory's huge ovens. Lucky for me; I didn't live anywhere near Woodingdean, so my occasional five-minute exposure was rather enjoyable. For the local residents, however, several hours of the aroma could be rather challenging if not really nauseating. After five consecutive mornings of this intrusion, residents would find themselves glued to the morning weather bulletin praying for a southwest gale to give them some respite.

The advert was aimed at local GPs with working knowledge of the area. I was still working in the hospital with variable shifts, so it took a bit of juggling when I became the successful applicant. It was a useful addition to my CV, especially when I described myself as the "Executive Medical Director of Operations," a title the factory administrators would find hard to recognise.

My role was fairly straightforward: the occasional medical for new employees and troubleshooting for workers with a poor work attendance. Before taking up my position, I was given the opportunity of a short tour of the factory operations. In the past, there had been a few health and safety issues, one of which had resulted in a rather horrible death. I was shown the actual machinery that had caused this regrettable accident. The operator had to climb up two steps onto a platform overlooking a conveyor belt of uncooked loaves of bread on the way to the ovens. The role of the victim had been simply to prevent the belt jamming, which would lead to a considerable loss of the product. A simple waist-high wooden barrier protected the employee. If he leaned too far over the belt, pressure on the barrier would cut off the electrical circuit and the machinery would come to a halt. To start things up again would require climbing off the platform to press various buttons to send the conveyor on its way again. This particular operator had found it rather tedious climbing on and off the platform several times a day, so he had jammed the safety mechanism with his socks so that any amount of pressure would not halt the process. The rest was history: he fell over the barrier and the conveyor belt only managed to grind to a halt when the hapless operator was physically jammed in the machinery. Fortunately, according to the traumatised witnesses, he lost consciousness very quickly. Unfortunately, he never recovered. I was reassured that following several improvements, a repeat of this sort of accident was now close to impossible. I hoped they were right.

After a few uneventful weeks in my new role at the factory, I was asked to see a 20-something young man who was failing to turn up for his Monday morning shift increasingly often, claiming rather spurious illnesses. I saw him on a Friday morning looking rather unremarkable. Let's call him Jack. We chatted amicably about the local Brighton football team and his lifestyle for the first 10 minutes. He lived alone, in a rented bedsit, in central Brighton. He didn't go out during the week but at weekends, he met up with five of his mates at his local, had a few beers and watched any sport that presented itself on the TV. They would meet up about 4pm on the Friday and leave about midnight. On the Saturday and Sunday, they would be in the same pub from about midday to midnight. This became his home over the weekend.

"How many pints do you drink on a Friday night Jack?"

"Not a lot, Doctor."

"How many do you reckon, roughly?"

"Well, it's hard to say. I don't really count," he said.

"Just roughly," I said, casually.

"Not as many as I used to and not as many as my mates, especially Old Bill and Ben, they certainly know how to knock them back," came the reply.

"Okay Jack, that's all very interesting but how many pints do you think you knock back. Is it more than two pints on a Friday evening?"

"Crikey Doc," (Doc now, is it?) "I'm not a lightweight."

"Would you consider yourself a heavyweight then?" I just wanted him to answer the bloody question (other expletives are available, some stronger!)

"I'm probably somewhere in-between, I reckon."

"How many do you reckon your mates Bill and Ben put back?"

"I don't know Doc, you'll have to ask them," he replied evasively.

I wasn't going to ask this rather frustrating young man how many cigarettes he smoked; otherwise, we would spend all day getting nowhere.

After another ten minutes of sparring, he finally owned up to drinking 10 pints of beer on a Friday night, another 15 on Saturday and again on Sunday, week in, week out. Forty pints every weekend.

"You Jack," I said gently, "I'm afraid to say, are an alcoholic."

"Are you taking the piss Doc? If I'm an alcoholic, then all my mates are too."

"Well yes Jack, they too are all alcoholics, but I'm only interested in you at the moment."

I chatted a bit about alcohol limits and side effects, short and long term. I also pointed out that his poor Monday morning work attendance rate was probably because he was hungover after a weekend on the booze. I gave him a leaflet from my bag and arranged to see him in four weeks' time to see how he was getting on.

I wasn't holding my breath, as the pub was obviously a huge part of his weekend social life. I didn't get a feel that Jack really comprehended the problems he was building up with his drinking. However, he did take on board the fact that he was in danger of losing his job. Four weeks later, he bought himself a second-hand mountain bike, as did all his mates, and they spent much of the weekends exploring the South Downs. His work attendance at the factory was now 100% so, naturally, I decided to take full credit for this turnaround. I was rewarded with five loaves of the factory's finest bread (no fish however!). Rather symbolic, I felt.

Dr D – A TALE OF TWO TURNERS

The first practice I joined had been created by a GP whose main driver had been to maximise his income from NHS capitation fees by accepting all patients regardless of where they lived. As a result of this ridiculous policy, we had patients living as far apart as Saltdean and Shoreham, two inadequate surgery premises and only two frazzled doctors. After two years of extremely hard work, made more demanding by the wide distribution of patients, Martin and I agreed that we needed to make substantial changes. My suggestion was that we should abandon both surgeries, find a single central building and only retain patients within a short radius of this new surgery. Martin quite reasonably preferred to continue at the Lewes Road surgery, but as a single-handed practitioner. Taking over the rump of the practice and the impractical surgery in Wilbury Road was not appealing, but we parted amicably.

It was around this time that my father died, and my older daughter was born, following which my wife developed her severe post-natal depression. We were also struggling to renovate our first house and pay the mortgage.

In the early 1970s, there were several good quality practices in Brighton with four or five partners and there was considerable competition to join them. General Practice was becoming a more popular career and was shaking off the image of being a depository for graduates who were not able to aspire to a hospital career, a path I had never contemplated.

My next partner approached me on the recommendation of his new landlord, a surgeon for whom I had worked at Brighton General Hospital. Arthur Tabor had been running an almost exclusively private General Practice with a surgery in his own home, as had his two partners, both of whom had recently retired, and bequeathed him their patients. This was really a coalition of three independent doctors who covered each other's practices during holidays and at night.

The senior partner, Dr Cummings, had simply reached retirement age, but Dr Turner had accepted an offer to run the student health department at the new Sussex University. The university had forgotten to appoint anyone for this role and approached the GP who looked after the students at the local teachers' training college. This was Dr John Beynon, the husband of the obstetrician I had worked for. He recommended one of his partners, also named Turner, but the letter of invitation had landed on the doormat of the wrong Turner, who thought this was a charming idea and promptly accepted the job.

Having once witnessed the snubbed Dr Turner stagger out of The Hove Club wearing his British warm overcoat and instruct the taxi driver to go to his home in Grand Avenue 'in the British Quarter,' the multi-ethnic students of the new seat of learning may have had a lucky break!

Arthur needed a partner and, after two years at the coal face I felt I was fully fledged. I could cope with the demands of private patients; however arcane they might prove to be. I was reluctant to abandon the deprived patients I had looked after in the council estates of Brighton and had never considered practicing outside the NHS, but I was unsettled, and accepted the offer of a trial for six months, at the end of which there would be the option for either side to end the arrangement. As I said, it was not a financial or ideological decision. I just thought I would give it a try, even though I harboured quite serious reservations about the morality of private practice.

I must have got over these doubts fairly fast as I took to it like a duck to water. However, the stress of the previous two years caught up with me; less than a month into my new job, I was feeling seriously weak and easily exhausted. I wrongly suspected this might be caused by glandular fever and, at my insistence, a blood test was reluctantly taken by my GP who phoned me later the same day. As he had correctly anticipated, I did not have glandular fever, but was severely anaemic and "since there is no sign of leukaemia, you must be losing blood internally, probably from a duodenal ulcer."

These were the days when the profession looked after its own. Two days later, a friendly radiologist, Joe Rubin, carried out a barium meal X-ray in his private consulting room, free of charge. He saw a small deformity of the duodenum compatible with ulceration. With Arthur's blessing and my wife's agreement, I went off to stay with my mother to recover.

I had never had convincing symptoms of an ulcer and after a

peaceful week and regular meals, I felt a complete fraud. Arthur had worked for a very senior haematologist at Barts Hospital and, when I drove back to Brighton a week later, he said I didn't look anaemic, never had, and took another blood sample, which showed absolutely no abnormality.

My transient "anaemia" had been the result of a technician, long before the arrival of automated analysers, handling two blood specimens and inadvertently taking two samples to test for haemoglobin from the same bottle. Then they had correctly looked at the blood films from each of the samples, which sadly did confirm a leukaemia in the other patient. Fortunately, I was able to go straight back to work.

The private patients I inherited had differing motives for paying for their medical care. Many, having always paid for medical care, simply chose to continue to do so after the inception of the NHS. This was partly because of the "privacy" and, in some cases, the feeling that they could afford to pay and should not avail themselves of the free care much needed by their less affluent fellow citizens. It was a status symbol for some of the "nouveau riche brigade" and others simply distrusted this new system, which they wrongly suspected was sacrificing quality for universality. Friends warned me that private patients would be impossibly demanding, a fear that evaporated on my first evening on call when the patient apologised for calling me after surgery hours and hoped I had finished my supper – that was a new experience!

Dr R – BOXING CLEVER

Between February and November 1990, mortgage interest rates peaked at an all-time high of 15.4%. I had two young children and had just bought my first tiny house. I needed every extra penny that came my way. At very short notice, I was asked to be the Medical Officer for one evening at a local boxing competition. I had a two-minute training session with the regular medic who needed to attend a funeral in Yorkshire and would not be back in time. My role was to make sure all 12 young men were fit to box before their fights. How do you do that in five minutes? I was then free to "enjoy" the rest of the evening and be present on the very rare occasions I might be needed in the ring. Each fight was contested over three rounds of three minutes. I didn't think much could happen in nine minutes. I have to say that the promoter looked after me well and was extremely grateful that I was able to help out. There was a not unattractive fee attached to my services, so it wasn't all hardship. He sat me down on a stool at the bar so that I had a good view of proceedings. Despite considerable effort on my part, I was never able to finish my free pint of lager. Every time I passed the halfway mark, the bartender replenished it. I thought it would be a little churlish to query this. This was the first live boxing match that I had ever been to. Although a keen sportsman, both taking part and watching, I had never taken much interest in this particular sport. Up close, it looked brutal to me, but the alcohol helped numb my increasing reservations. People watching, has always been a hobby of mine, and that evening offered me a feast of new and bizarre material. However, by the time the last fight was in progress I was a little worse for wear and looking forward to my bed. The attentive promoter had provided a taxi both ways, another reason why I didn't have to worry about my alcohol intake. Suddenly the fight was stopped as one of the poor lads had been knocked out and it was lasting for much longer than the regulatory 10 seconds. The doctor was summoned to the ring over the loudspeaker.

"What me? What now?"

"Yes you," said the promoter. Getting off the bar stool having not moved for 90 minutes wasn't easy, but climbing into the boxing ring, which had been constructed about five feet off the ground, was nigh impossible in my state. The young boxers had made it look so easy earlier in the evening. However, with the help of a couple of audience members I made it. By this time, the poor lad was coming to, thank goodness. After a brief horizontal chat, he was able to get to his shaky feet unaided and we both helped each other back to the dressing rooms for a "full" examination. Just to make sure, and to cover my arse, I sent him off to Casualty. As I was sobering up in the taxi on my way home, it occurred to me that the whole purpose of this sport was to inflict temporary, and hopefully not permanent, brain damage on the opponent, resulting in a knockout. A knock-out was defined as falling to the deck and not being able to stand within the referee's count of ten. I can tell you; I would not want any of my kids taking up this madness. Ever since then, I have boycotted this so-called sport, including watching it on the TV, I made an exception for Rocky 1, 2 and 3, but that's different, isn't it?

Dr D – DEREK IN CUSTODY

I had never met a man wearing a white suit until I got a call out to a flat in Hove. On arrival, I met a deeply tanned 25-year-old man, who, unlike me, had probably seen Saturday Night Fever. He had just come back from a holiday in Spain with his three older brothers and had a high fever. They were a rather glamorous bunch, fashionably dressed and casual. I never met the sister or their parents, but I gathered that the father had been an erratic, bullying Glaswegian drunk and their family was a pretty dysfunctional one. They were all hard-working, heavy drinkers and smokers and their emotional lives were all turbulent.

Derek soon got better and became a regular patient of mine, which was a mixed blessing.

My wife and I had been invited for dinner with old friends on a Friday evening in June, and I was already late in picking up the baby-sitter. My last call was to an elderly couple, Fred and Doris Day, who lived in a double flat in Kingsway Court and were looked after by an adorable old nurse who lived with them. Fred Day was reputed to have been a spy in WW1 and had then been a major force in one of the biggest music publishers in the world, Frances Day Hunter. He was now 96 years old, and gently fading. My daily visits were more for the benefit of Sister Morgan and his wife, both of whom adored the old man.

As I rushed past the bar on the ground floor of Kingsway Court, I heard Derek hailing me. I turned down his invitation to join him, spent a few minutes with Fred then managed to get back to my car without being seen by Derek, who was halfway through one pint with another in front of him.

At about midnight, after I arrived home from an excellent night out, I had taken the babysitter home and was just about to get into bed, when the phone rang. A very apologetic Mrs Kavanagh, who was manning the answering service that night, said she knew I was not on call, but would I phone Hove Police Station.

Derek, with about six pints of lager inside him, had decided that although he lived less than 200 yards up the road, he would drive there. He had parked so ineptly that he was spotted by a patrol car, breathalysed, and arrested.

"Sorry to bother you Doctor, but we have a private patient of yours in custody who is charged with driving under the influence, and he refuses to have the necessary blood sample taken by anyone but your good self." The police officer didn't need to identify the miscreant.

Derek, still obviously drunk, had for some hours succeeded in fending off the police surgeon, who was not at all pleased to see me usurping his role and probably his fee. He had been doing this in the vain hope that his long-mistreated liver would have time to significantly lower his blood alcohol level.

As was customary, I took blood from Derek's arm, filled two bottles, and then held them behind my back. The policeman chose one, and I handed the other to Derek.

Foolishly, I then asked if they would like me to take Derek home. I wasn't surprised to hear that they thought this an excellent idea, and the sooner the better.

Home for Derek was a third floor flat above a large pub at the top of Second Avenue that he shared with his delightful first wife, whose mother ran the pub. Life with Derek was predictably chaotic, and his wife coped with the help of benzodiazepines (the group of drugs which includes Valium) washed down with white wine. She never seemed to be incapable but was permanently slightly sedated and occasionally a bit confused.

With considerable difficulty, I got Derek into and then out of my car and onto a bench in the garden at the rear of the pub.

"Where exactly do you live, Derek?"

"There," slurred Derek, pointing triumphantly to the three levels of metal fire escape walkways.

"You shtart climbing and I'll tell you when to shtop."

It was a warm night, and I was sorely tempted to leave him where he was and get to bed but I started climbing and, after a lot of misleading directions, finally stopped outside a huge sash window on the third floor.

It wasn't locked and was open just enough for me to get my fingers under the lower sash and heave it up.

At that point, I felt something being pushed into my stomach. This turned out to be a double-barrelled shotgun in the unsteady hands of Derek's wife. After what seemed like a long time, my protestations registered in her brain. "Oh, it's you Duncan. Do you want to come in?"

She seemed just a little disappointed to hear that I was returning her husband!

Dr R – AN UNUSUAL VISIT

As a surprise before a planned birthday lunch, I escorted Rachel, my second wife, on a private tour of Brighton sewers. These tours were rarely available, and it took on my part, a great deal of effort to organise. On the back of this, I had hoped for some sort of appreciation, which, it was obvious from the outset, was not forthcoming. I suppose it didn't help that I turned up fully prepared in sensible waterproofs including hat, rubber gloves, and sturdy wellington boots. The guide, Florin from Romania, who spoke perfect English, was naturally sensibly dressed too, and he also provided us with facemasks to reduce the risk of infection. My wife arrived dressed in entirely inadequate clothing, a floral skirt from Laura Ashley, and ballet pumps. I reassured her that all would be well and that it was going to be a memorable experience, which it did turn out to be. I would recommend this unique sortie along lengthy passages overlooking the steady flow of Brighton waste. The smell, I must admit, is rather challenging to start with but as I was just getting over a cold, it didn't really bother me. My wife, however, was in rosy health without any nasal impairment. The fantastic Victorian brickwork of this sturdy canal certainly withstood the test of time. The whole tour lasted around 30 minutes and I guess we walked about 100 yards. This time was punctuated with fascinating titbits of information from our guide, who turned out to have a PhD in marine biology: a proper Doctor, no less! The walk terminated at a metal ladder with approximately 50 rungs, which looked rather daunting. Modesty dictated that Rachel climbed last so we both blindly followed Florin to what turned out to be a heavy metal manhole. On lifting this plug, we all emerged onto a busy pavement just outside the Royal Pavilion. Most Brighton locals are aware of the history of this rather splendid building. The Prince Regent, George IV resided there from the late 18th century. His mistress, Mrs. Maria Fitzherbert lived a convenient 100 yards away at 55 Old Steine, which later became the first YMCA in Brighton. There has always been speculation that there was a secret underground tunnel linking the two properties to simplify their liaison. The passage, to this day, has never been found. Anyway, we all arrived safely back in the Brighton sunshine and beautiful fresh air. Our peace, however, was broken by "Ello Dr Brooks, what are you up to?" The voice came from a patient of mine called Mandy, a 22-year-old, who was with her four children, stepmother, and step-step grandmother. "Oh, Hi Mandy, I have just been visiting a patient and got a bit lost, nothing to worry about." Mandy simply winked knowingly at me and off they all went. My wife and I didn't really feel like lunch right then and postponed our special birthday meal until the evening.

The tour obviously had a profound effect on Rachel as she used to bring it up from time to time, especially in public.

Dr D – A PROUD PARENT

Today, the A&E department is the clearing house for problems that range from sore throats to life-threatening injuries. Patients who either can't or don't bother to consult a GP sit next to severely ill patients on trolleys who should be in a ward bed. The whole gamut of patients: the "well but worried"; addicts; drunks; the genuinely ill or injured; the terminally ill, who are not adequately cared for in the community; and those urgently in need of surgery: they all wait to be dealt with by hopelessly overworked staff.

It was not always like this. In my early days as a GP, it was assumed that we would attempt to sort out the problems we could cope with and only refer to Casualty those we had seen but felt unable to treat adequately. Patients who we decided needed hospital admission did not have to linger on trolleys; their admission was negotiated by the GP contacting the junior doctor working on the appropriate ward. This might involve several phone calls if beds were scarce.

The contract between patient and GP was simple and, unless a locum had been arranged, the GP was responsible for the care of his or her patients, 24 hours a day, 365 days a year. My patients had a medical card with my name on it; they were my patients, and I was their doctor. This direct personal responsibility was something we took very seriously, and breaches of this trust generated huge disapproval among medical colleagues with lasting reputational damage to the errant physician. Patients were probably a bit more forgiving, many realising that we had committed ourselves to an almost undeliverable resolution. The forces that led to the unravelling of this relationship were mainly political, and deeply misguided.

Most authors tend to reserve their list of thanks and apologies for the end of their book, but I feel it appropriate to acknowledge the problems this pressure of work caused for our families.

In my case, it was never a lack of concern for or interest in my family, but they were inevitably, and sadly, at the end of a formidable queue of people for whom I felt immediately responsible. Sorting out my patients' problems, finding a locum and getting up to date with correspondence was a nightmarish prelude to holidays. For the first two days, I would be exhausted and probably very hard to cope with.

After one snowstorm that left Brighton paralysed, I remember insisting that if I could go to work, my daughters could go to school. With some difficulty, I delivered them to the High School. In response to my usual inquiry at suppertime as to how their day had been, two stony-faced teenagers said accusingly in unison, "We were the only people at school."

A few years before this lapse of parental charity, they were both sitting on the floor of the office at 98 The Drive, Hove, being fed orange juice and chocolate biscuits by our welcoming but inquisitive secretary. I was looking at some notes when the following conversation began.

She asked my older daughter, who was about 11, "What is Delia up to at the moment?" This was one of her more progressive and disreputable classmates.

"She's reading one of those books." Delia, who had reported having the first serious snog of everyone in their class, had found a pornographic novel hidden in the parents' bookshelves.

"What sort of book do you mean?"

"One of those grown-ups' books," replied my flustered, blushing daughter.

"What's it about?" my secretary asked ingenuously.

"Err, well it's an adult story."

At this point my younger daughter lost patience with her sister's evasive waffling and chimed in with, "It's about what parents do in their bedroom."

"And what do they do there?" continued my secretary, unwisely.

"They probably have a F U C... Dad, do you spell 'fuck' with a K?"

There has never been a prouder parent; those school fees were worth every penny.

Dr R – AN OFFER I COULD NOT REFUSE

In about 1981, I was appointed Medical Officer to the RNLI. It was an honorary post. I would have declined any reimbursement, anyway (possibly!). However, it was a great honour and one that I was eager to share with anyone who cared to listen. The crew kindly took the new young doctor on a manoeuvre, which was about how to recover a swimmer in trouble from the sea. What I didn't realise was that the swimmer was going to be me, since the captain took an unnecessarily steep turn, over some rather large waves, tipping me into the water. It was a great bonding experience with the crew, who were mostly undiagnosed psychopathic adrenalin junkies!

A week later, after the whole of Brighton had heard about my new appointment and my subsequent rescue from the sea, I was relaxing at home with a brandy, after a lovely Saturday evening meal with my family, when the telephone rang. This was 11pm, and I was not on call. I picked up the telephone.

"Is that the Lifeboat Doctor?" (The voice came through plenty of static crackle on the telephone line.)

"Yes"

"We have a medical incident 10 miles off the coast of Brighton. Can you respond? We know where you live and can hoist you up by helicopter in 10 minutes." (Again, there was loud static crackle on the telephone line.)

"Okay." (I knew I was way over the limit to drive a car, but I was sure I was fit enough to be hauled up and sort out what needed to be done.)

"What I want you to do is lay out a white sheet in the back garden." (We had quite a small garden surrounded by trees, but I was confident they knew what they were doing and anyway, I was fairly inebriated.) "When you have done that, I want you to shine a torch up into the sky so that the helicopter can isolate your position. Over and out." (Again, there was loud static crackle on the telephone line).

This was all new to me and they gave no advice on the dress code, so I didn't bother, although I do remember changing my underpants! Just as the 10 minutes were up and several airliners had gone over on their way to Gatwick Airport my 11-year-old step son noticed some twitching of curtains several houses up the Avenue, where a colleague and now ex-friend lived. Apparently, they were having a dinner party and the host was using an old wireless tuned into a dodgy wavelength and a muffled mouthpiece, to great effect. There had been bets to see if I really was egocentric, naïve, and vain enough to fall for it. Nobody won any money because they had all agreed that I would fall for it. Bastards!

I thought it was very cruel at the time and still 40 years later suffer from flashbacks.

Dr D – DENTAL DISTRESS

She was quite a pretty girl, a little overweight but, unlike her equally attractive and bubbly sister, she was morose, and her parents were alarmed by her increasingly withdrawn behaviour. While her sister was busy buying clothes, experimenting with make-up, dancing and flirting, Mary chose to be at home in her room wearing dreary clothes and appearing red-eyed at mealtimes.

Her parents ran a small guesthouse and, although I wasn't their family's regular doctor, I had occasionally been asked to see one of their residents, so I wasn't a total stranger when she reluctantly agreed to see me.

I insisted on seeing her without her understandably anxious parents. For the first couple of minutes, I waffled on about something trivial before asking what was worrying her, at which point I stopped talking.

Slowly she divulged how she felt. She slept badly, felt tired all the time and nobody wanted to see her, which didn't surprise her because she was so boring and ugly. She cried. I provided tissues and then let the silence return before suggesting that I would like to examine her in case she had some illness. I asked her mother to come into my room. I wasn't really expecting to find anything wrong and was surprised when, prompted by her very bad breath, I saw that she had so much dental plaque that her teeth were barely visible. This explained not only the halitosis but also her slightly indistinct speech.

"She's never been to a dentist in her life," said her Mum. "Terrified of them"

I told her that one of my daughters had felt the same and I did understand just how terrifying the prospect of dental treatment was for some people, but it was important that she had her teeth cleaned. I told her that I knew a gentle dentist who would not cause her any pain. She agreed to go if I went with her and so, a week later, I took her to see my friend, having promised that this visit was only to meet my dentist, Jim, and his nurse, and that there would be no treatment of any kind but that she would have to let him see inside her mouth.

She was terrified. It took 10 minutes before my very patient friend could judge the extent of her problem – when he succeeded, he had never seen the like before. It was obvious that she was going to need some effective sedation and, now that I had become her white knight, only I would be an acceptable provider.

I took advice from a friend who was experienced in administering dental anaesthesia and sedation and explained to Mary what I intended to do. The following week, she was again in the chair sweating with fear and crushing my fingers.

Valium given intravenously is a very effective and safe form of anaesthesia, but it took an impressive dose before she was sufficiently relaxed and drowsy for my friend to start chipping away at the plaque. It was more like sculpture than dentistry, with chunks of plaque flying out of her mouth or rattling down the sucker. Her gums were very inflamed but, once relieved of a covering that had been in place for years. her teeth were white and perfect.

She lived quite close to the dental surgery. On three consecutive Mondays, neighbours must have been intrigued by the sight of me, with Jim in his white uniform, guiding home a young woman so relaxed she could barely stand.

About three months later, I was driving a babysitter home. As I passed Mary's house, I was delighted to see her snogging a young man in the porch. Job done!

Dr R – AN UNLIKELY STORY

I was attending a half-day release course in Guy's Hospital London with a bunch of young GPs, who wanted to become trainers. This was spread over an academic year, so I got to know the thirty-odd doctors attending, some better than others. We were often split into small groups; a regular attendee in my group was an Indian GP, who seemed an extremely nice man. He told me he had lost his first wife, who was also an Indian GP working in their two-doctor practice. They had three children, but he had happily remarried. This time it was to another Indian doctor, and she too joined his practice to replace his deceased wife. Several years later, this very pleasant man hit the headlines. Apparently, he had attempted to murder his second wife by cutting her throat. I think this happened outside their family home, but I'm pretty flaky about the actual details. This is the general thrust of the story. Because of the freezing weather that evening, it prevented her from bleeding to death. She had survived to tell the tale and my seemingly benign colleague was arrested. The police looked into the circumstances of the death of his first wife, and he was later convicted of both murder and attempted murder. What a shock that was for me, and what a misjudgement of someone's character!

The post-graduate centre based in the grounds of Brighton

General Hospital was usually very busy around lunchtime. Most weeks, there would be a lecture relevant to General Practice preceded by some half-decent food. I was once sitting with a group of visiting GPs from practices in South London. As usual, at one of these gatherings we were exchanging medical stories over lunch. While I was in full flow telling the story of my Guy's Hospital experience, one of the chaps on the lunch table was continuously trying to interrupt me but I wasn't having any of it and waved him away. Not giving up, this chap stood up and said, "I've got to stop you Rod before you go any further. I think I ought to introduce you to Mrs Singh (not her real name). That name rings a bell, I thought. Oh no, this was the leading lady in my anecdote! When one is in a hole that deep, there is absolutely no point in attempting to climb one's way out, so we chattered for a while. What surprised me a little was that she had continued to bring up her husband's children as she still felt she was their stepmother, despite the circumstances and being divorced. The imprisoned doctor would regularly call the family home to speak to his children, as was his right. I can't imagine what it was like to hear his voice on the phone, the voice of a murderer, who tried to kill you: all for the insurance money. To my shame, I was tempted to ask if I could have a peep at her scar. If I had, I think the hole I was standing in would have completely swallowed me up!

Dr D – CELIA'S DETOX

Had Jennifer Saunders met one of my most memorable patients she would not have needed to resort to invention in order to create the wonderful characters in Ab Fab.

Celia trained as an actor, but her main career was in scriptwriting. She was glamorous, acerbic, and wonderfully witty. When I first met her in the early 1980s, her husband had recently died from alcoholism and she and her demure daughter were struggling to cope with his absence. In Celia's case, she simply self-medicated with champagne, which she drank all day, rarely eating, and smoking heavily. She made it clear from the start of our association that she didn't approve of doctors who didn't drink so I heroically overcame my feelings of hypocrisy as I discussed her failing liver function with a glass of Lanson Black Label in my hand.

The house was large, but we always seemed to meet in the kitchen because she was visited at about 11 o'clock each morning by a huge gull that tapped impatiently on the window until she opened the back door and let him in. She fed him every day on tinned sardines and chocolate digestive biscuits, so it was not surprising that Cecil – "he is a C-gull, darling" – was the size of a small albatross.

As her liver function blood tests reflected ever-worsening liver disease, I tried every approach I could think off to persuade her to stop drinking alcohol or at least drink less, and to eat. Being admitted for assisted withdrawal was not an acceptable proposal; she would not see a psychiatrist; and my attempts to emotionally blackmail her by involving her daughter were equally futile.

The only person she now trusted was me; "So, what are you going to do about it?'"

There is really no prescribable substitute for alcohol; tranquillizers rarely succeed in a home setting and are potentially dangerous if the patient keeps drinking.

"Why don't you swap alcohol for marijuana?" I suggested. "It would be a lot less harmful." And for the first time one of my suggestions evoked a muted display of enthusiasm.

It so happened that another patient of mine, after a brief period of incarceration following his being convicted of fraud, had created a successful business. He was in a nursing home being treated by me for pneumonia with a regime of antibiotics, twice-daily physiotherapy, and a total embargo on smoking, which included his favourite weed.

He was now well enough to be bored stiff, so he responded positively to my request for help. When I examined him three days later, I considered him well enough to be discharged, for which he thanked me. Then he presented me with the fruit of his labours in a cigar box.

I went straight round to see Celia, who was pleasantly surprised to find, when she opened the box, that I had kept my promise to supply an alternative therapy; it contained 25 beautifully made and uniform spliffs, complete with small cardboard filters and neatly twisted paper at the tip. You won't be surprised to hear that on my next visit later that week I encountered a rather spaced-out Celia, an empty box, and an open bottle of fizz.

Despite her continuous mild intoxication, she was quite active socially. On one occasion, when I arrived a bit later than planned, my appearance coincided with her and her daughter heading for her car, a red E-type Jag. She had persuaded her daughter to put on a dress and she herself looked fabulous in full make up, wearing a red trouser suit, red patent leather boots and a red cape.

"We're going to a family funeral."

She had no relatives of her own, so I presumed the deceased had been related to her husband and she was keen to introduce her daughter to this grieving family, none of whom they had ever met. She managed to get to the church just before the coffin and strode down the aisle dragging her reticent daughter. Then she stood at the end of a front row pew until two seats were made available. It was only halfway through the first hymn that she read the order of service and discovered that they were in the wrong church. Without batting a mascara -laden eyelid, she grabbed her daughter and walked back down the aisle.

Her only regret was not being there to hear the surprised and confused family members speculate about who this exotic figure had been, and what part she had played in the life of their dearly departed relative.

Dr R – TWO WRONG TURNS

It was my turn to be on call for the August Bank Holiday Monday. The weather was fabulous and all I wanted was to be on the beach with everyone else, so my temper was a little ragged and I felt a bit resentful. To add salt to my wound I was very busy but hadn't really seen anyone particularly ill all day. Around 6pm, I had almost caught up with my visits and was looking forward to grabbing a few minutes with my family over supper. As luck would have it, an urgent request (no, demand!) for a visit came in. Apparently, a worrying lesion had appeared on a 25-year-old man's hand. I dropped everything I was going to do, raced across Brighton, and ran up three flights of stairs (no blooming lift of course), to be greeted by an inebriated woman and a very drunk man (the patient). The emergency turned out to be a very benign looking wart on his right thumb! I suggested amputation of half of the thumb would guarantee a cure and marched out through the door in disgust. However, in my anger the exit turned out to be a broom cupboard. In an attempt to regain my dignity, I said something that I would later deny in court if necessary and left, hoping the warts would spread all over his body, starting with his face. I'm not usually that evil but these fantasies sustained me for the rest of my shift.

The following morning, the practice was due a visit from

representatives of the Royal College of General Practice. This was an inspection of the premises and the state of the medical notes to see if they came up to the standards required for the practice to become a training post for doctors on the local Vocational Training Scheme. I had already been approved as the Trainer GP, so it fell upon me to show the inspectors around. What a stupid morning to pick. On the day after an August Bank Holiday weekend, the waiting room was heaving with patients. I was exhausted from my 24-hour shift on call and had only grabbed a couple of hours' sleep the night before. So, I was not looking at my best. The two inspectors were college doctors, smart and fresh in their three-piece suits, who had clearly never done a night on call in General Practice in their lives. However, I had to get through this, whether I liked it or not. Inspection of the medical notes went well, and I finally took them up to the administrative centre on the top floors. (I'm not sure that the typists who worked there knew it was called that). An annex to the typing pool was the private room of the Chief Executive Managing Director (probably better known as the Practice Manager), in which we had installed the latest computer equipment. This was our pride and joy and I felt it wouldn't fail to impress. However, I once again took a wrong turn and found myself in the broom cupboard. You would have thought I would have learnt by that point. For the record, the practice was approved, and the rest is history.

Dr D – A NIGHT WTH DEREK

About 10 years after the police station encounter, I had another late-night session with Derek. During the intervening years one of his brothers, who was profoundly deaf, had committed suicide following the ending of a relationship, and Derek's marriage had unsurprisingly also ended. The police called at about midnight to say that Derek's oldest brother, who managed a large hotel in central London but rented a small house near Brighton Station, had been found dead. Derek was described as being extremely upset. He was refusing to go home and had asked if I would see him.

It was raining hard, and I had to park some distance from the house in Kemp Street, so I arrived looking bedraggled.

I asked the policeman who let me in if I was required to certify death, but this had already been done and the body moved by undertakers. There was expected to be a coroner's inquest because the cause of death was almost certainly suicide.

The deceased was not a patient of mine, but we had met a couple of times and I remembered him as being an amusing, rather gentle gay man and probably the calmest of all the siblings.

I found Derek sitting hunched up on a large white corduroy covered armchair, drunk, and weeping silently.

I said how sorry I was, because I knew how fond he was of

his brother, and what a terrible shock it was that he had died so young. I got no reply and decided to wait until he felt like talking to me. The policeman came in, asked if it was OK for him to leave, and left us alone.

"He killed himself, you know. How could he do that?" said Derek eventually.

"Had he been depressed for a long time?" I asked, hoping that it would encourage him to talk.

"Didn't know he'd ever been depressed," mumbled Derek before getting up and staggering across the room, returning with two tumblers full of whiskey.

For the next half hour, between bouts of sobbing, he expanded on his love for this brother who had protected him as a child and bailed him out of many of the numerous scrapes he had found himself in over the following years.

"It's no good, I've had enough; I can't go on anymore."

I don't know where he had been hiding it, but suddenly there was a gun in his hand. Apart from once having spent an hour firing an ancient rifle at elusive targets in an indoor firing range as a cadet in the school CCF, I knew nothing about guns, which quite frankly terrified me. I hoped this might be a replica, but it looked worryingly authentic to me, and my role now was clearly to stop Derek blowing his brains out rather than merely lending a sympathetic ear and getting him into bed.

For the next half hour, despite my soothing, anodyne conversation, all attempts to get hold of the weapon failed and Derek either waved it around or stuck the end of the barrel in his ear.

Eventually he dropped off into a drunken sleep and I got hold of the gun, a small revolver, and hid it behind a bookcase after removing the two bullets in the chamber and pocketing them. I laid him on the shagpile carpet with pillows wedged to keep him on his side and one under his head. It wasn't the first or last time I left him in a similar state.

Outside, the rain had stopped. I drove home through empty glistening streets and was back in bed, asleep 10 minutes later, at about 2am.

In the morning, I told my wife about the night's drama and reached over to the bedside table to show her the bullets.

"Doesn't look much like a bullet to me," she said in a dismissive tone of voice that I found irritating after having been in fear for my life for half the night, but she was right – they were both solid brass dummy rounds.

Dr R – AN EYEFUL

In 1984, I developed a sore red eye, five days before a ski trip to the French Alps with a bunch of lads. Despite various treatments, my eye deteriorated sufficiently for me to cancel my holiday. A week later, I found myself being referred to St Thomas' Hospital, London. Several junior doctors had a peep into both eyes, but they all looked perplexed and called in a senior eye doctor for her opinion. She didn't say anything to me, but I did hear a sharp intake of breath and, "Admit him now and watch him like a hawk." Well, that was reassuring! One of the junior medics explained that they wanted to do an anterior chamber biopsy under a local anaesthetic. "Over my dead body, you're not sticking a needle into my eye unless I am under a general anaesthetic," I responded with as much dignity as I could muster. I was quite prepared to go home with a patch over the afflicted eye. In fact, I felt it would give me a roguish look that I didn't find unattractive, especially back in Brighton. Despite my reluctance, I was taken in and immediately ambushed by a research medic who wanted to do a lumbar puncture on me. "You can do what you like while I am under the GA," I responded helpfully, although I did wonder why. My lower back was a long way away from my eyeball, and what the connection between the two was I didn't know. I was now in patient mode so naturally I didn't ask! I came out of the anaesthetic pain free (the pain was to come later) and linked up to an intravenous drip. Another junior doctor came around, as I was rumoured to be an interesting case, and helpfully told me that looking into my eye was like looking into pea soup. I felt better after that as I quite like pea soup! The following day, the head consultant came by on his teaching round so that everybody in the whole hospital could peer into my eye and mutter. Before the consultant saw me, they were all huddled around the corner, out of sight, but not out of earshot. I caught small phrases like "could spread to the other eye," "may go blind," "cannot rule out a cerebral tumour yet," and "what about AIDS sir?" The response to the latter was, "He does come from Brighton," mumble, mumble and then suddenly they were all there crowded around my bed. "Good morning, Doctor Brooks, all seems to be going well. Any questions? No, excellent," and off they went. I was too intimidated and too timid to say anything. Later in the afternoon, a very young registrar came to see me on the ward and asked if he could have a quiet word. I didn't like the sound of that but followed him up the corridor outside the noisy ward. He took a long time coming to the point and finally blurted out, blushing to the tips of his ears, "Any homosexual contacts, Doctor Brooks?" "Oh yes, hundreds," I replied enthusiastically. This got his attention until I reassured him that I had many homosexual patients, Brighton being the "gay capital of the UK", but I hadn't actually been buggered by any of them, "Well, not yet!" I added to confuse him a little more. The outcome was a request to do an HIV test.

"Of course, as long as the result doesn't reach my GP's

notes because both positive and negative HIV tests can have a detrimental effect on many insurance policies." "No worries Doctor." I hate that phrase; and anyway, I hadn't been worried, until he said it. My eye stabilized (by the way the condition was retinitis, and a causative agent was never isolated) so they discharged me. However, I started to develop a horrible headache, which was only relieved if I was lying down. I didn't like to mention it in case they thought I was making a fuss. Moreover, before heading home, they wanted me to trek across to Queen's Square ("It's easy by tube") to have a retinal arteriogram, a series of photos of the back of my damaged eye. "Sure," I said, "No worries," and "Thank you for everything you have done for me."

I left the nurses a box of Black Magic chocolates, although I did notice that they already had a few boxes stockpiled in one of the store cupboards ready for consumption. The retinal arteriogram was quite interesting despite my pounding head. They injected some fluorescent orange dye intravenously that seconds later was distributed along the tiny arteries at the back of my eye, which were then automatically photographed. I was now free to travel home and to my bed. At Victoria Station, I was particularly lucky to catch a non-stop train to Brighton almost immediately and was able to call my wife to pick me up at Brighton Station. I wanted to lie down on my bench seat on the train, but despite the carriage being almost empty I was too embarrassed to do so. I needed a pee though, so I staggered off to the loo. I have to say that I don't find it easy to pass urine while being bounced around in a small compartment hurtling its way to the coast. The result was inevitable. I pee'd onto my brand new, very expensive Hush Puppy suede shoes. Ordinary urine can be dealt with quite satisfactorily, at a more convenient time, but my urine was now a deep fluorescent orange. On returning to my seat, I'm pretty sure that nobody in the carriage could fail to see my speckled footwear. Despite many attempts to clean them, the stains failed to shift, so a couple of weeks later I donated my shoes to a charity shop. This was not the first time I had had an irreversible mishap with a pair of suede shoes, so I diplomatically chose a different establishment.

My filthy headache, which took a good week to settle, was apparently to do with a leak of cerebral spinal fluid from my lumbar puncture. I recovered pretty good vision in my afflicted eye, so I count myself as fortunate. I don't ski on snow now. At 75 I prefer a much more enjoyable form of SKIing, i.e., Spending Kids' Inheritance! The reader should try it! My HIV blood test finally arrived, negative of course, so I had it discreetly framed and indiscreetly hung over the main loo at home so that future guests could use the facilities with confidence. I was able to access my own personal medical file from my GP and of course, the hospital had sent the HIV results there as well. I promptly shredded it. No worries!

Dr D – ARISTOCRATIC ANGST

Richard Doll, the eminent British epidemiologist, wrote his first paper detailing the connection between tobacco smoking and lung cancer in 1950. Another paper published in 1954, based on a study comparing the health of doctors who did or did not smoke, proved beyond doubt that smoking was a very dangerous habit. It then took 53 years before legislation was passed that outlawed smoking in enclosed workplaces.

My medical partner for 10 years from the mid-1970s, was an extremely competent and caring doctor but, as many doctors still do, experienced some reduction of sympathy when confronted by patients whose lifestyle choices clearly damaged their health and made no attempt to implement his advice to mend their ways. As an athlete who took great care of his own health, he simply could not understand anyone who thought differently.

A contemporary of his at medical school was running a successful private General Practice in Chelsea and, if any of his many gay patients came to Brighton, they were encouraged to join our practice.

The Hon Simon X, who came from a wealthy family, had never done a day's work in his life. After many sybaritic years in London, which had left his health in tatters, he decamped to a large, detached house just off the London Road. My partner took one look at this scruffy, long-haired, and very unhealthy man and decided that I might be a more compatible GP for him. So, he managed to squeeze him onto my visiting list.

The house was chaotic. There were no curtains in most of the rooms, and no carpets apart from a few threadbare rugs; the walls were covered in zodiacal signs, handwritten slogans, and quotes from Aleister Crowley, the occultist, painter, and novelist. What I could see had once been valuable pieces of antique furniture were now damaged beyond repair, a bit like the man himself.

He had a black lover who visited at weekends and did his best to clean the place and to supplement his friend's daily diet, which consisted solely of the rum-based drink called Malibu, which he diluted with fruit juice. Whatever his failings, Simon was one of the most charming and courteous people I have ever met, and we got on well despite his reluctance to take medical advice. His family was caring and kept in touch, and he was occasionally visited by the family solicitor, Lord Goodman – reputed to be the most influential man outside Government at that time. A short, fat, calm and brilliantly clever man he was supportive and genuinely sympathetic, but even he, like the rest of us, failed to persuade Simon to help himself. By this time, his liver failure was advancing rapidly; he looked pale, mildly jaundiced and his bare feet were swollen and infected. Returning from what was probably my third visit, I told my partner that his patient had asked me if I would take over his care. The folder containing Simon's extensive notes that had been sitting on my partner's desk was launched in my direction before I finished speaking.

At the start of my next meeting with my new patient, he asked hesitantly if I had had the opportunity to discuss my new status with my partner. I confirmed I had done so and that, with great reluctance, he had agreed to the transfer. Simon said he hoped this had caused no problems for me and I reassured him that it had not.

"Thank you, Doctor Stewart; that is a great relief. If I can speak freely?" I nodded.

"I have to tell you that being looked after by your partner is rather like being cared for by the SS."

I don't think I ever passed on that compliment, and Simon died quite peacefully a couple of months later.

Dr R – A HANDFUL OF DIAGNOSES

A friend of mine from Hove Grammar School for Boys went off to university only to fall ill with some mystery illness, which involved quite dramatic weight loss. I visited him in hospital, and he looked as if he was dying. It turned out my mate, Malcolm Crohn, had coincidentally developed Crohn's Disease and the diagnosis been staring the clinicians in the face, as his name was there at the foot of his bed, for all to see.

George would do the Guardian newspaper's crossword every morning in 15 minutes flat. He was in his early 70s, very tall and clumsy, and was forever banging his head. In the space of six months, he became disorientated and, once, when he was out shopping, he couldn't find his way home. The time taken to complete his beloved crossword became longer and longer until he was unable to even attempt it, leaving him in great distress. Eventually and reluctantly, he sought medical help, and an MRI scan revealed a chronic subdural hematoma. The blood clot was removed, and he subsequently improved but unfortunately only to about 90 percent fitness. The delay in diagnosis had been to his cost.

My General Practice had a young boy with Down syndrome. He developed cancer in one of his undescended testicles. We had been concentrating too much on his mental health to check on the basics. It was noted at the boys' paediatric assessment that at birth both testicles were still in his lower abdomen, but this was not followed up and subsequently they were not surgically brought down to his scrotum, if they hadn't arrived by their own means. Undescended testicles have a much greater risk of developing a malignant tumour.

The residents of the YMCA mostly had highly challenging mental health issues. By their very nature, various conditions were difficult to treat, and this took up much of my time, at the expense of offering routine health checks, especially to the YMCA's women. George William House, one of the larger YMCA residences, houses about 70 men and 20 women. With the help of my practice nurse, we were able to examine 18 of the women and found three breast lumps (one malignant) and four abnormal cervical smears. All were referred, with good outcomes. This experience made me much more aware that mental health does not protect patients from poor physical health. In fact, it makes it worse.

A 35-year-old female patient of mine had recently had an ileostomy for a severe form of colitis. She was a fairly simple but pleasant enough woman who came to see me one day complaining of a weeping smelly stoma. The hole in her side was indeed unpleasant to examine. A swab taken later revealed the gonococcus, as did a swab taken from a discharge from her husband's penis. Both were successfully treated for gonorrhoea, and I was able to give him some sound advice, man to man, about the dangers of "having a bit on the side!"

I used to support a forty-something woman with a low IQ and a reasonably well controlled psychotic condition. Her personal hygiene was an area she could perhaps have paid more attention to, so it was with some dread when I needed to collect an over-due routine cervical smear from her. We made an appointment for when it would suit us both. When she arrived, instead of having a pre-appointment shower or bath, she instead covered her lower abdomen and upper thighs with a sweet-smelling talcum powder. I sorted her out on the examination couch and prepared myself to examine her cervix. The combination of aromas was so heady that I had to temporarily excuse myself, leave the room, take a deep breath, hold it, rush back in, do the necessary, and rush back out again for another deep breath. I am not sure what the three patients waiting outside my room thought was going on. For the record the result came back as "inadequate please repeat." I duly made her another appointment but unfortunately couldn't do it myself as I was on annual leave. However, the experience pales into insignificance compared to the time when, on investigating a young woman's vaginal discharge, I pulled out a rotting tampon that had been quietly hiding in her vagina for at least three weeks. At least I cured her in one "foul swoop"; although extremely embarrassed, she was deeply grateful, as she had been fearful of a life-changing diagnosis. The downside was that it put my consultation room out of action for at least an hour before I could return without gagging.

Not many patients got up my nose, but this arrogant young solicitor did. He came to me complaining of a discharge from his penis. Among the usual questions, I took a sexual history and learnt nothing of significance, although I suspected he was lying through his teeth. However, what really annoyed me was that, while I was gently swabbing the end of his genitalia, a large drop of white pus seemed to fall in slow motion onto one of my brand-new blue suede shoes. They were both expensive and extremely fashionable in the day. The report that came back from the pathological laboratory was the "friendly" gonococcus, i.e., he had somehow contracted gonorrhoea. On the strength of this report, I donated my beautiful shoes to the Oxfam charity shop in Hove. The staff were so delighted that they didn't notice the tiny blemish from a previous life. I am pretty sure all the germs had perished by then. What really got up my nose was that he didn't want his wife, the mother of his three children, to know of his condition. I treated him with the appropriate antibiotics as he refused to attend the VD clinic (as it was then called). Happily, his wife needed to attend for a routine cervical smear, and I was able to take a swab at the same time. This was clear, thankfully, and I avoided what could have been a tricky situation that probably would have ended in tears. The cocky solicitor returned for his follow up appointment to check everything had cleared up. I explained that in order to provide a specimen from his penis I would have to "gently" massage his prostate. Unfortunately for him, I had to massage with some vigour to produce a sufficient sample. I did notice that I should have swabbed his eyes, as I noticed a watery discharge had appeared in them when he staggered off the examination couch. In addition, to obtain a sufficient penile swab I needed to penetrate the urethra of his penis several centimetres to be absolutely sure that there were no residual gonococci bugs lurking there. I have to say I was pretty pleased with myself on how I had handled this difficult medical conundrum. I had cured the patient, probably made him think twice where he "dipped his wick" the next time, and if he did, I had hopefully inspired him to use the necessary protection to protect his wife. Moreover, because of my clumsy examination techniques, he never came to see me again. The cost of replacing my shoes paled into insignificance compared to the satisfaction I felt.

Dr D – BRIGHTON FUNERALS

As a humanist, I was always relieved and delighted when the funerals of my friends and relatives really celebrated the life of the deceased and were not diluted by religious trappings.

Undertakers are understandably reluctant to discuss their activities but ask, and you may hear stories of some very odd funerals. One told me about an actor who died in his 50s after spending much of his career in Shakespearean roles. A non-religious ceremony was held at The Downs Crematorium.

The coffin on its catafalque occupied the middle of a small room and around it stood half a dozen of his closest thespian friends, all holding the script of one of the Bard's plays. They all had a role and read their parts in turn but allowed a silence at the point where the deceased, who had been granted the major role, would have contributed.

A funeral I did attend was that of a patient who lived in Kemptown in Brighton. She had been a bit of an "it girl" living in London in the 1960s. She looked a bit like Twiggy, with big blue eyes and immaculately cut short blonde hair.

In her 50s, her heavy smoking had caught up with her and she developed lung cancer that was treated with high doses of radiation, which appeared to have enclosed the tumour in scar tissue; she remained symptom-free for many years, but still smoking and drinking heavily. Her first marriage had ended in divorce, and I got the impression that this was a cause of deep regret to her. Her second husband was perfectly pleasant and hardworking, but a rather pedestrian character and she always gave me the impression of being an unhappy woman who clung to her addictions.

Sadly, her cancer reasserted itself and, as she was not considered suitable for any active treatment, palliative care was arranged. Her general health was poor, and she became extremely anxious and angry, but she did eventually become resigned to her fate. She died at her home quite peacefully three months later.

The funeral was also held in the chapel at The Downs Crematorium, which is a small well-lit modern room. It lacks the sombre grandeur of its older, neo-Gothic neighbour Woodvale, but it seemed the more appropriate venue for a non-religious event, which took place on a warm summer afternoon.

When I arrived, her husband was sitting by himself next to the coffin and Procol Harum was providing the soundtrack. I sat next to the couple's cleaner who I liked and had got to know well as we coped with the stresses of her employer's last weeks. She introduced me to the two gay neighbours and then we all sat without talking.

On the other side of the room her mother was sitting in a large fur coat, weeping quietly; next to her was the stepfather, a small skeletally thin man in an unfashionable chalk stripe suit.

Frank Sinatra and "My Way" took over. Eventually her husband stood up and said a few words, but he started crying and sat down.

A couple of minutes later, by which time Procol Harum were back, he tried again.

He was telling us how much he had loved his wife who, as we all well knew, could be difficult, but she had made him very happy. At this moment, we heard the sound of a car approaching very fast and then stopping with a squeal of tyres. This was followed by the slamming of doors and a strange rattling sound. We all turned to look at the late arrivals, two uniformed prison guards each handcuffed to a man of about 30 whose ankle shackles were the source of the mysterious sound. This was her son; of whose existence I was entirely unaware.

As soon as this trio were seated, the husband resumed his speech and told us that, as the assembled company would have formed the nucleus of his wife's ideal party, we should have one. Immediately there was the sound of corks popping and the undertakers, looking slightly uncomfortable, provided us all with a glass of champagne, and a couple of refills before we left the chapel to view the floral tributes and her son left for Dartmoor.

Dr R – YMCA EXPERIENCES

It was not a popular decision with all my partners when I took on the YMCA. The title, Young Men's Christian Association was massively outdated as far as the Brighton branch was concerned. It was basically a housing association for all ages, all sexes and sexual orientation, and open to all religious beliefs. It was not run as a Christian organisation. Perhaps one day the Brighton YMCA will go it alone, but it would mean changing its name, perhaps something with "Brooks" in it, partially to reflect the enormous amount of selfless work I did for the association. I have to say the staff did a fantastic job, often under deeply challenging circumstances. There was great leadership from William Collyer and then later, John Osborne, as Chief Executive.

Early on in my relationship with the YMCA as their medical officer and advisor, they rang me to urgently assess one of their residents from 55 Old Steine. I agreed to see him at the end of the morning surgery. I was told I couldn't miss him, as he was about 6ft 8ins tall, wearing a heavy donkey jacket (this was during a very warm spell in the summer), wellington boots and a tea-cosy on his head! I passed on the description to my receptionist who thought I had nothing else to do but muck about making up fictitious patients! However, right on cue, Robert turned up, clearly severely psychotic but otherwise well. I referred him directly to the psychiatric services without the need to section him as he went voluntarily, much to my relief. Otherwise, that could take hours to organise if the psychiatric social workers were busy, which they always were due to massive under staffing in my view. It was about four weeks before I saw Robert again. On this next occasion, I was on the promenade with five of my mates, all dressed in wetsuits of various bright colours, sorting ourselves out to do a spot of windsurfing, as the wind was up. You have to remember, Robert had only met me once for about 20 minutes in the surgery, when I had been dressed appropriately. He marched past us all on the prom, wearing exactly the same gear as he had on our previous meeting in the Surgery. He cheerily greeted me with a "Hello Dr Brooks, how's it going?" I told everyone we had just employed a rather eccentric junior partner. Nobody queried it; they were more interested in getting out on the water, as I was.

I know you are not supposed to have favourite patients, but there are some that you can't help being extra fond of. My first encounter with Brian was in a routine surgery that I was running at the YMCA's building. He was a new patient, having moved down to the coast from where he had lived all of his 55 years in South London. He never married and had no children. He was clearly a schizophrenic and things, it would seem, had started to go wrong for him in his late teens when he got into trouble with the police several times for being in the possession of various illegal drugs. He lived most of his adult life in some sort of sheltered accommodation, having fallen out with his parents when he was 16. He had pretty much lost contact with his folks and didn't know if they were still alive. Despite a rather unsatisfactory life, he came across as a gentle, very funny, and reasonably intelligent man who had had the misfortune to be cursed with a psychotic illness. He had never held down any sort of job for a significant amount of time but was always willing to volunteer for various projects that the YMCA was running. Most of his demons were kept away, with the help of the terrific support the staff gave him and some antipsychotic medication. I used to see him every week at my clinic in an attempt to build up a trusting relationship. It was a good three months before his medical notes arrived from London. They were voluminous but there wasn't much in them that he hadn't managed to remember and tell me about beforehand. However, the last note was from the medical officer of Brixton Prison, where he had been incarcerated for nine months having been convicted of attempting to hold up a building society with a banana! I wish I could have been there.

After two years in General Practice, I decided to become a trainer. This involved going up to Guy's Hospital on a half-day release for a year and bringing our own surgery up to scratch. The most arduous task was writing up a short medical history on all of my patients. This was inserted in the back of the notes so that any doctor seeing a patient that he did not know much about could quickly catch up without wasting time wading through the whole folder, some of which were very large indeed. It took me many hours, all in my own time, to complete this task but it was worth it because 12 months later I had my very own trainee to mould into a brilliant GP, all because of my own talent. However, this proved to be less easy than I thought it would be, and much to my surprise, from time to time, a whole bunch of medical students were dumped on me as well so that they could gain work experience. I decided to take my first lot of students up to George William House where about 70 YMCA patients lived in sheltered accommodation. Among this unique population were a dozen or so schizophrenics and two or three bipolar patients. Also, for good luck, were a couple of lifers from Broadmoor who had served their sentences and were back in the community with, I must say, very little Home Office back-up. This was the 1980s; hopefully, things have significantly improved. Anyway, I thought I would show these spotty youngsters what real General Practice was all about. This all went swimmingly until I demonstrated to these students how to take blood safely. Of course, what did I do, but to plunge the needle of a full syringe of warm blood into my thumb? I thus demonstrated perfectly how NOT to collect a sample. I think these boys and girls learnt a lot from that teaching morning, one that they will never forget, I suspect.

A few days after my humiliation in George William House, I packed the medical students back off to their medical school in London, potentially to spread the word about that "prick" of a GP in Brighton! I never heard any rumours to that effect so hoped that they had been loyal and discreet.

On my first free afternoon, I wandered through the outpatient department of the Royal Sussex County Hospital in heavy disguise, to the old VD clinic situated directly at the back. I was relieved not to bump into any patients that I knew, and that none of the nurses and doctors in the clinic recognised me. I was there to have my HIV status tested. I knew next to nothing of the medical history of the YMCA patient I had inadvertently shared blood with, and that was irrelevant anyway, as all patients were treated the same whether the "donor" was high- or low-risk. The galling part of this check-up was I had to wait a further three months (over 90 days, more than 2000 hours) for a second HIV test to see if it had converted to positive. I had to wait seven days, (168 hours) for the result of my first OPD appointment that, not to any great surprise, was negative. However, the next three months seemed to drag, and a dark cloud hung over me for all of this time. It was the last thing I thought of when I went to bed at night and the first thing in the morning when I awoke. The fateful day finally arrived. Wearing yet another disguise, I swept through a packed OPD once again, with my head down and some trepidation. This was not helped by a voice springing out of nowhere, bellowing "Ello Dr Brooks, wot yer doin going to the VD clinic?" This could only be the vocals of the one and only Tracy. She was 20 stone at 19 and had had her jaws wired together in a last-ditch attempt for her to lose some weight. This was inevitably unsuccessful as she confided in me at a later date, that she invested in a liquefier and managed to mush up all her favourite unhealthy food to such a state that she could feed herself via a straw through the small gap in her mouth. You could never win with Tracy, but she had some wonderfully friendly outgoing qualities that meant you just couldn't help liking her. She went on to have two lovely children by an all-suffering fiancé who could not have been more than eight stone in weight: a beanpole of a lad with a brain clearly not contributing much to his overall poundage. I tried not to imagine them having sex as the logistics of it all were absolutely beyond me. However, they seemed happy enough so good luck to them.

So back to the question, to which about 100 eager patients were now awaiting an answer. "Um, research Tracy, research," I managed, with as much confidence as I could muster. I scurried off adding, "Cannot stop Tracy, lovely to see you, late already." I was never quite sure (and never asked) if she believed me, as she wasn't completely daft, far from it; but either way, I think I went up in her estimation. Having managed to jump over that particularly nerve-wracking hurdle, I still had to wait another 30 minutes (1,800 seconds) for a result that could change the course of my life. A numb, out-of-body feeling came over me while I fantasised about what lay ahead of me if I was HIV-positive. I wasn't, and I am still here some 30 years later. What I did learn was to have total respect for anything to do with needles, as I didn't want to have to go through that experience again.

George William House, which was in Portslade, is now unrecognisable and has expanded into a much larger concern and been renamed George William Mews. A third major development was William Collyer House, in North Road, in central Brighton. These premises were formally opened by HRH, Princess Anne. My wife, Rachel, and I were both presented to HRH, and we exchanged a few words. I listened with much interest to HRH's take on the care of this particularly vulnerable group of society. Unfortunately, there was not enough time for her to hear my experiences, perhaps another time? I must admit these kinds of visits from the Royal Family do raise the profile and public image of the YMCA, so I guess nothing but good came from it.

My wife Rachel, who was one of the art teachers at Varndean High School, Brighton, found some time to run art classes at George William House; the present Chief Executive John Osborne, remembers the peace and tranquillity she bought to these highly valued occasions. Freddie, our son, also did some paid work in the reception area of the newly opened William Collyer House. This was a bit of an eye-opener for him that didn't do him any harm. Matthew, my second son from a previous marriage also spent a happy year working in the gardens of George William House.

One evening, I was called out to see an 80-something woman named Nora, who was complaining of an acute shortness of breath. She was a resident of George William House. I had known her for a couple of years and had been treating her for heart failure. Over time, I got to know her well but felt she didn't seem to fit the profile of a person who needed this type of place to live in. One thing I have learned over the years is that we all have a story to tell, but I didn't know what hers was. As it happened, that particular evening, things were pretty quiet, and she responded very quickly to my treatment. I had time on my hands. So, I took the opportunity to ask how she had found herself living under the care of the YMCA. She was very reluctant to talk initially, but she eventually stared to relax a little. Her eyes started to well up with tears and then the words started to flow too. "I was a happy go-lucky child, the youngest of four and lived the first 20 years of my life in North London with my parents. My father was a bus driver and my mother a school teaching assistant. We were very content, and I can only remember a very happy childhood. At 20, I married my one and only boyfriend, who earned good money as a butcher. I gave birth to a lovely girl just after my 22nd birthday, and my husband and I rented a ground floor flat with its own garden in Tottenham, North London, close to my parents. My daughter Sarah attended a lovely nursery and started infant school just before she was five years old. The school was two blocks from the flat, so it was perfect. I was able to walk her to and from school; it was a great joy for me. I only wanted one child, so she was especially precious to me. At the end of her first term at school, I walked her home as usual. She was excited as it was coming up to Christmas and we were going to go shopping later that afternoon. We always walked hand in hand, for safety, along the pavement of Tottenham High Street. Somehow, she tripped, and her hand slipped out of mine; the next second she was lying in the road having been hit by a bus. She was rushed to hospital but never recovered." Nora stopped speaking and looked at me for the first time. She had told her story as if the tragedy had happened the day before. "I never recovered, Doctor." In those days, counselling was neither available nor even thought of. After a while, when Nora had recovered sufficiently, I stood to leave. She grabbed my hand. "You have children, don't you Doctor? Please don't make the mistake I made of holding my child's hand with her on the roadside of me. If she had been on the other side, she would be still alive today." I later learnt she split up with her husband soon after the accident and never remarried.

This nightmarish story has never left me, and I often retell it to others, especially young parents, and grandparents. However, after this sad revelation, I did learn from the staff at George William House that Nora's mood had lifted almost miraculously; she had, for the first time, started to engage with the staff and the other residents. I only wish I had had that little chat with her earlier. Maybe she hadn't been ready for it then, but I could have tried.

Dr D – A MISDIAGNOSIS

The community of retired Masons were, as they had been promised on arrival, very ably cared for at Harewood Court. There were communal activities, housekeeping help for those who required it and, on the ground floor, about half a dozen rooms with full nursing care. My contribution was to hold a surgery in the building, once a week, for all the residents who belonged to my practice, which the majority did.

I suspect this model, where the residents could move between independent living, assisted accommodation and full nursing care within the same building, was extremely expensive but it worked wonderfully well.

The residents had several communal lunches with quite lavish catering, the best being on Christmas Day. After grace had been said, they all sat down and drank their sherry while I carved the turkeys, my wife plated up the vegetables and my daughters helped the regular staff delivering food and refilling the wine glasses. For one very small old lady, this was probably the only occasion on which she drank any alcohol, and every year someone was placed on guard to support her when she tried to stand up to toast The Queen. At the end of the meal, she was taken to her room in a wheelchair, usually fast asleep, and put to bed.

On one occasion, as I was walking down one of the long corridors to see a very elderly lady with heart failure, I had to step aside to make way for a tall, overweight, and barely mobile 85-year-old lady called Mrs Wilson. She was being escorted and supported by two of the staff.

"Good morning," I offered cheerily.

Mrs Wilson turned her impassive face towards me for a moment and then continued to shuffle on her way. Although she had severe dementia, she had been the Mayoress of a large Midlands town and was reputed to still be able to complete the Daily Telegraph crossword before lunch. However, I never actually checked to see if she completed it accurately.

I moved on to visit my patient, Miss P who, in contrast to Mrs Wilson, had no intellectual impairment, but was bedbound. She had once told me that she had worked as a secretary to David Lloyd George when he occupied 10 Downing Street.

Having just seen a TV programme about him in which he called every woman "Caryad" and attempted to seduce most of them, I asked if he had ever targeted her. She reassured me that the great man had behaved entirely appropriately towards her, "but since you ask Doctor, and you are clearly concerned for my maidenhead, let me reassure you that while I may not have married, I will not be going to my Maker unopened."

Back in the corridor, I met the stately Mrs W and her nurses returning to her room. I repeated my earlier greeting; by way of response, she turned to one of the girls accompanying her and said in a loud voice, "Thinks he's God's gift."

At the end of one Monday morning surgery, a flamboyant

resident, a retired actress who made herself up and dressed like a circus clown with heavily rouged cheeks, a striped top and pink knee length socks, was ushered in by the nurse who assisted me. To be completely accurate, she did most of the work, so that my main function was to rubber-stamp her inevitably correct decisions.

Our resident thespian had hosted a big family lunch on the previous day that she had found stressful. Afterwards, she had complained of severe indigestion.

I was running late and, after a rather cursory examination, as she looked well and was not in pain, I prescribed an antacid mixture and rushed off to my surgery.

My secretary met me at the door and told me I should go straight back to where I had come from. Arriving back, I found my unfortunate, wrongly diagnosed patient was now lying dead on the floor, having just had her second and lethal, heart attack. I offered a silent apology and swiftly removed the prescription from her lifeless hand.

Dr R – FROM SKELETONS TO LEGENDS

After I had qualified, I still felt that there was a further role for the skeleton that I had bought in my first week at Medical School. He lived in the spare bedroom. My two boys, would often visit him while he was asleep in his little wooden home. They were always careful not to wake him. When the boys attended their nursery school, they obviously spoke warmly of their other "brother". As an educational treat for the pre-school pupils, the headmistress invited me to bring in "Slim" to show what a friendly young man he was. They didn't turn a hair, even when I threatened them by saying, "this is what you will look like when you have grown up if you don't eat your vegetables!"

One evening a week, I ran a sterilisation advice surgery at a nearby clinic; afterward it was customary for me to give the receptionist a lift back to her parents' home, some 10 miles away. I had dressed my old friend in one of my jackets, together with sunglasses and a cigarette packet in the top pocket and sat it up in the back seat. Halfway into the uneventful journey I asked the young lady to reach over to the back seat for my cigarettes*. This she did only to scream so loudly that we nearly had an accident. She spent the rest of the journey in the passenger well of the car, gently whimpering in the foetal position. This prank had badly misfired as the young lady's mother turned out to be the administrator of the clinic, and that almost got me fired. I decided to sell the skeleton after that, so as to remove any further temptations, although I missed my old pal who had become part of the family.

Early on in General Practice, I was supporting a chronic alcoholic. He was a butcher by trade, and I did worry about him being drunk in charge of all those lethal knives. Things were getting out of control, and he asked me if he could be admitted into hospital for detoxification.

"I can do that for you at home if you like Benny," I said.

"That would be great, Doc," he replied. This was the first and last time I would ever attempt this as it does have its pitfalls. I prescribed him various medications and wrote out a programme for him to follow. Having made an appointment for him to see me in three days, I said that he could call me at any time if there were any "unlikely" problems. Off he went in good spirits (probably not a good choice of words as it happens!) I had the evening off and, after a very pleasant meal and a couple of glasses of wine (making sure I was below the driving alcohol limit), I thought I might pop in to see Benny at his home on a local council estate, to give him some moral support. Trish, his wife, and mother of six children, made me very welcome. Benny was in an armchair, drinking copious amounts of lemonade and watching the footie on a huge TV, which seemed to take up most of the room. "Would you like a drink, Doc?" he offered. Silly question, I thought, as he poured me a pint of Tesco value lager without waiting for a reply. In the other corner of the lounge was a highly decorated homemade bar of the kind that was popular in the eighties. No sooner had he delivered my pint than he suddenly collapsed falling backwards into his cherished construction. The crashing of bottles and glasses helped focus my mind. I leapt (or maybe staggered) to my feet, and dragged him feet first out of the bar, at the same time ordering Trish to dial 999 for an ambulance. All this commotion woke the sleeping, and previously unnoticed large Alsatian and even larger young teenager, Donna. The loyal canine, seeing that I was assaulting his master instinctively started to attack me. I'm not good with dogs at the best of times and was relieved that Trish was able to bring him under control before there was any significant damage to me. I started CPR* with some desperation as I was suspicious that my detox programme might have contributed to the scenario. Fortunately, Benny regained consciousness just before two burly ambulance women arrived. I thought it best he was transported to hospital to be checked over. Mother and daughter (not the dog, however, who looked disappointed I was about to leave) were very grateful for my visit asking, "What would have happened if I you had not turned up out of the blue?" I'm always happy to bask in the glow of gratitude and off I trotted (or rather drove) back home.

"How'd you get on?" asked my wife.

"Oh, OK love. What are you watching on TV?" My wife was working in the large comprehensive school adjoining Benny and Trish's estate. Born to a Rhodesian mother and being quite dark herself, she remembers with trepidation her first day at the school. As she entered the estate, the first sign that greeted her had been vandalised in red paint, with the words. "Keep Whitehawk White." She decided to be known by her middle name 'Rachel' as she felt less of a target than if she used her African name. The following day during her "any news" session, a young teenager, Donna no less, leapt up to tell the whole class in vivid detail how her GP, a certain Dr Brooks, had saved her father's life. For a few weeks, Dr Brooks was a celebrated "living legend" in the classroom, and my wife declined to reveal her true identity.

---

* Yes, I did smoke a few cigarettes then, mostly to look "cool". I stopped when my wife was pregnant with our last child over 40 years ago and it was one of the best things I ever did. I now view anyone who smokes as absolutely bonkers as the health hazards are enormous; it also makes one and one's clothes stink of stale tobacco, which seriously isn't the slightest bit cool.

For the record, I smoked "Peter Stuyvesant" King-Size filter cigarettes at the time, when I could afford it. The brand was all about the packaging as one could tear a small hole at the top of the pack through which, by a quick flick of the wrist, once could propel a cigarette into the air landing (hopefully the right way up) between my lips. I had perfected this manoeuvre while driving but it did take me a good 18 months.

*CPR – cardiopulmonary resuscitation involves thumping on the chest to the rhythm of a popular song

Dr D – A CORPSE AT A PRESTIGIOUS BRIGHTON HOTEL

People do behave strangely in hotels, and often need medical advice at the most inconvenient times, from a doctor's point of view. I was phoned early one Sunday morning by the under-manager at a prestigious Brighton hotel; there had been a death and they wanted me to come as soon as possible. Certifying death is not usually a matter of much urgency, but he insisted I visit as soon as possible as there were "complicating circumstances."

On that Saturday, the hotel had hosted a medical conference for specialists that had culminated in a dinner at which two friends from their medical school days met for the first time since they were undergraduates. They were now both in their early 60s, married and at the top of their respective branches of the same medical tree. They had had a fling as students that was never consummated at the time, but this was finally achieved that night after an alcohol-fuelled evening, which had taken place in her hotel room. Their union had been such a great success that they repeated it early in the morning and fell asleep. However, when she awoke, her new lover was irrefutably deceased.

I found her in an understandably distressed state in her room, with the corpse still in her bed. She was accompanied by the under-manager who was a very nice and gentle, but rather indecisive character. Apart from the shock caused by his death, there were concerns linked to the fact that her husband and his wife had both left their homes and were at that moment en route to the hotel to pick them up. We clearly had to get the body back to his room without being seen. I suggested that my friend, the under-manager, find one of the big circular laundry trolleys with wheels.

He left rather unenthusiastically but eventually reappeared with an empty trolley. He suggested that perhaps we should leave things as they were and call the police. I said I thought discretion overrode legality and that I took full responsibility. He was persuaded to help me put the body into the trolley. This is not an activity that most people have had the opportunity to practise, and it was fiendishly difficult because the deceased was both tall and overweight. We had sent the distressed woman downstairs with her suitcase. We eventually laid the trolley on its side, fed the body in feet first and then lifted it upright. Next, we put in his evening wear, shoes, and underclothes, then piled bed linen on top. We reached his bedroom without being seen, got him into bed and then struggled to get him into his neatly ironed pyjamas. I wasn't getting much help from my nervous assistant, so I sent him off to cope with any arriving spouses and considered how best to finesse my deception.

I arranged the contents of his spongebag around the bathroom sink, and opened a couple of the bottles of pills, all of which were treatments for heart disease. I hung up the trousers and jacket he had arrived in and hung his dinner suit in the wardrobe. Then I filled a drawer with the rest of his clothes and put his wallet and spectacles on the bedside table. A glance at my watch reminded me that I had forgotten to pick his watch up from the other room. I had just retrieved the watch and had added it to his other possessions on the bedside table when the phone rang. I was told that his wife had arrived; would I mind dealing with the situation?

I gave the room a quick scan and felt I hadn't missed any obvious detail. I had, in fairness offered to be the one to break the news to his wife, as I didn't trust the under-manager to be a convincing liar. I went downstairs, introduced myself and gave her the dreadful news. She was shocked and terribly upset, so we sat for a while in the corner of the lounge until she calmed down. Then she said she would like to see her husband, so I escorted her up to his room. He looked peaceful and the room did appear to have been occupied overnight. She bent over him and kissed him on the forehead.

"You know, Doctor, people do act strangely in hotels. I always packed his pyjamas, which he never wore, but what is really odd is that at home he always wore his watch in bed."

I didn't offer any reply and simply hoped that the gravity of the situation would obscure the matter of the unworn watch.

Dr R – YOU ONLY GET ONE CHANCE

Iris came to see me for the first time following her fifth early miscarriage in a row. She was in her mid-20s, and desperate to start a family. I like to think that I didn't advise her to get another partner, but I'm not absolutely sure! However, I didn't see her for some time, and I cannot remember if I referred her to a consultant gynaecologist for some advice regarding her fertility. Anyway, here she was again, very happy, with her new husband Jason and pregnant again. Lara was born, but only survived a few months, having never left hospital. She had a rare condition in which her abdominal organs protruded into her umbilical cord. This was a pretty tough time in their life but, unperturbed, she gave birth to Sarah some 15 months later. I managed to pop into the maternity wing of the Royal Sussex County Hospital a few hours after the delivery with a bottle of Tesco's plonk. There were a few anxious moments until the paediatrician gave the thumbs up.

I saw this happy young family from time to time until I unexpectedly retired on health grounds in 1995, when Sarah was about 13. I kept in contact over the next 18 years, with a newsy Christmas card even though I moved to Scotland for 10 of those years. However, a message from Iris on her 2017 Christmas card revealed Jason was far from well. She managed to move to a new apartment more appropriate to Jason's needs, but alas, he never made it and died in the autumn of 2018. My wife and I went to the funeral at one of the local crematoriums. I had not seen Iris for at least 23 years, and she hadn't changed much. I watched her walk with great composure from one group of mourners to another. A young woman in her early thirties who I did not recognise accompanied her. This young lady spotted me and came running over to give me a big hug. It was Sarah, of course. She had grown more than I had shrunk, and it was a great joy to see her despite the circumstances. Iris soon followed on behind her. I gave her an embrace and she broke down in tears. She had done that enough times in the past, so it was perfectly normal to do it now; of course it was. It is so important not to miss funerals. You only get one chance.

Dr D – TIME OF DEATH

Contact between GPs and the police usually involves the death of a patient under circumstances that prevent the doctor from being confident about the cause and therefore being unable able to sign a death certificate; this can simply mean the patient had not been seen recently. It may be necessary to hold a post-mortem examination if the coroner decides the cause of death is uncertain.

My first call on a Sunday morning followed a message from the police that an elderly man had been found dead in his kitchen and they needed a doctor to confirm death. The flat was untidy but clean enough. The body was lying in the middle of the floor of the small kitchen. I confirmed he was dead and asked if anyone in his family had been informed.

Unfortunately, his daughter was on her way from Southampton to see him, unaware that he had died, and, as there was no way of contacting her, these being pre-mobile phone times, I offered to wait for her to break the news.

A young constable and I sat in the kitchen and waited. He wasn't much of a conversationalist, and to break the monotony we both got up several times stepped over the corpse and moved about the flat.

Eventually the silence became too much for him.

"How long do you think he's been dead, Doc?"

"Just over an hour I'd say."

"How do you work that out then, I didn't see you take his temperature or anything."

"True, but I still reckon about an hour."

"So, how can you be so sure?"

"The kettle's still warm."

"Bloody hell, you've been watching too much crime on the telly, mate!"

The daughter arrived not long after this and my new mate left us alone in another room while she absorbed the news of her dad's death.

Dr R – THE SAME BED

I first met Tony on the day he got married to Karen. He was due to get married on the Saturday afternoon, and his best man brought him around to my home in the morning for a coffee but principally to keep him occupied. On return from honeymoon, the couple joined my list in General Practice. Tony was a great car mechanic and worked from his own business attached to his home. He kept my old bangers on the road for years, and we became good friends. Both he and I were the same age: thirty-nine and a half, give or take a few days, and we had decided to have a combined 40th birthday party. Around this time, Karen had a baby girl. On her last routine post-natal visit, the midwife thought that Tony looked tired and pale and recommended that Karen should alert her GP to do a blood test on him. I was passing their home with my wife the following Sunday afternoon, so took the opportunity to take a sample. On the way home, I delivered it to the pathology laboratory in Brighton. Halfway through the following morning surgery, a consultant from the haematology department was put through to me. "The blood sample we received last night shows acute myeloid leukaemia," was his bombshell.

"What's the prognosis?" I asked. "He will have a bone marrow transplant and die," came back the brutal reply. This consultant wasn't to know he was talking about a mate of mine but simply another patient. After surgery, I visited the happy family to wreck their lives. Tony was subsequently treated at the Royal Marsden in a specialised unit; he had a bone marrow transplant and died having never left the hospital. He never made it to 40, and I didn't celebrate my birthday that year. I remember visiting him when he was in a sterilised isolation unit. He told me the horror of his recurring nightmare. A figure in a black cape would appear every night in his sleep and encourage Tony to follow him up a dark passage. Every night, Tony managed to shoo this figure of death away. The Royal Marsden tried everything to keep Tony alive, but eventually decided to stop treatment and allow him to die, as he had been in a coma for several days. For me, it was a relief to see him sleeping peacefully in a normal bed with all his ghastly tubes and wires taken away from him except an ECG monitor. Friends and family had been alerted to Tony's terminal condition and we had all gathered around his bed, about eight of his best mates. The only person missing was Karen, who was up the road with a friend breast-feeding her little girl who was still less than six months old. Karen was contacted and told to come quickly, so, in the meantime, I stroked Tony's forearm and whispered continuously in his ear, telling him to wait for Karen to arrive. His eyes would slowly flicker over to me. They were without focus but it appeared clear that he understood. After a very long 10 minutes, Karen arrived and took my place next to her husband. Karen talked to him continuously for another five minutes, after which Tony suddenly sat up in bed. Karen thought she was witnessing a miracle for a moment, but his pupils were fixed and dilated, and his ECG had flat lined. "He's gone, Karen," I said as gently as I could as Tony sank slowly back into his pillows, gone forever. Every one of us gave Tony an embrace before leaving. Excluding me, that was the first death they had witnessed, and their calm dignity was extremely moving. My four-year-old son was outside with my wife. The three of us returned to say goodbye. It was my son's first death. As a doctor's child, he was growing up fast. Tragically, my wife's mother died in the very same bed six months later with multiple myeloma. She was only 60 and the perfect Grandma. Thirty-four years on, there isn't a week that goes by when I don't think of them both.

Dr D – GRAND HEAVYWEIGHT

Not all hotel visits were particularly interesting or rewarding but the management was always very appreciative that we attended as soon as was possible, given that we were already coping with a heavy, but in my case, a thoroughly enjoyable workload.

All our appointments were for 20-minute consultations unless the need for a longer or shorter time was foreseeable. I remain convinced that you can achieve a great deal more for a patient in one 20-minute consultation than in two 10-minute ones. I carried out many activities that I suspect my colleagues in the town were simply too busy to undertake. I took blood samples and did some simple tests myself, such as ECGs. I also syringed ears and did quite a lot of minor surgery and cryotherapy. I even did the occasional simple chiropody, in passing, for some of my more arthritic patients who couldn't manage it themselves.

Another GP friend of mine was one of the kindest men I have ever known. He carried a bag of tools in his car and was much loved by his older, isolated patients whose electric fires and bedside lamps he had rewired, dripping taps he had silenced, and lightbulbs he had replaced. Urban General Practice was a very different job in those days and the contract between patient and doctor was valued by both parties. Both sides understood the abilities, problems, and the failings of the other.

On a very busy Monday morning, we had a call to visit a man in the Grand Hotel, Brighton. My favourite under-manager was a bit short on detail but sounded genuinely alarmed, so I went straight round and parked my ancient VW Beetle outside the front entrance where, unusually, I was met by a waiting porter who offered to carry my second bag, in which I stored ampoules, syringes, and dressings.

I was whisked up in the lift to the third floor and then we turned into a long corridor. Halfway along, there was a small group of chambermaids and other staff members, some with ears to the door of a guest room.

"What's the patient's name? "I asked

"Oh, I think he's called Johnson," my companion replied.

Among the waiting group was the under-manager, who told me there had been what he referred to euphemistically as a "disturbance" that they thought I was best placed to sort out; all expenses were to be settled by the hotel.

I wasn't expecting the scene that met me when I opened the door. This was rock star level room trashing. Two windows and the mirror over the desk were cracked, there was glass on the floor from broken bottles and glasses, the overhead and bedside light bulbs and fittings were smashed and, in a slightly surreal touch, the whole room was covered in feathers from the ripped pillows. Sitting on the bed, staring out at the sea, was a huge immobile silent man with a tear-stained face smelling very strongly of alcohol. This man was obviously not going to be amenable to answering a load of questions so I suggested that, as he was clearly having a bad day and as he could not stay in this room, we could find him a new one so that he could get some rest.

I must have sounded sufficiently sympathetic and authoritative; without a word being spoken, he managed to put on some slippers and allowed me to guide him to the door. We crunched our way across the room, and I opened the door to a semi-circle of very anxious faces.

My last sight of him as he disappeared down the corridor was this giant of a man gently shedding white feathers and holding the hands of the two tiny Philippine girls, who like tugs with a liner, were escorting him to his next berth!

I gave instructions that, before he fell asleep, they should make sure that he took the two painkillers I had provided and drank at least a pint of orange juice. It always worked for me.

"Oh! you're ever so brave," lisped my favourite manager.

"Why brave?" I asked.

"Do you know who that is?"

"Yes "I said "His name's Johnson."

"No, not Johnson; Johansson – heavyweight boxing champion of the world"

Dr R – A FERRY STORY

I learnt to ski in my early 30s and, for the next 15 years, managed a week's holiday in the French Alps. I initially went off with a bunch of lads, but when, my children were old enough, we all went as a family, which was a very different experience, as we drove to the mountains in our beloved VW campervan. We would catch the Newhaven to Dieppe evening ferry on a Friday, and drive through the night, with the kids fast asleep in the bed behind us. The excitement of seeing the mountains in the distance, reaching the foothills, and then climbing up through the snow was worth the long drive. This was a proper family adventure, although putting snow chains on the wheels in a blizzard was rather challenging. After a week of skiing, exhausted but with no broken bones, we would drive all day back to Dieppe, usually arriving in the early hours of Sunday morning. I was able to park the VW first in the queue for the afternoon ferry and catch a few hours' sleep in various parts of the campervan. On waking, it was always very pleasant to have lots of coffee, and a wander around Dieppe. The morning concluded with a wonderful French lunch and lots of wine followed by a stagger back to the van for the ferry crossing. One year, we were surprised to find ours was the only vehicle left in the car park. (We had adjusted our watches to UK time the night before and were now an hour late!) However, we just made it. Now the very last car to be allowed on the boat, we made our way on to find some seats for us all. The ferry journey was just over four hours' duration. No sooner had I put my feet up ready for a kip, than the loudspeaker requested the presence of a doctor on board. Well, there was bound to be dozens of medics ready to leap up to offer their services, so I wasn't in any rush to present myself. Five minutes later the loudspeaker repeated the message. "You will have to do something Rod," chastised my wife. "Yeah, but…" I didn't get to complete the sentence.

"Yeah but no buts!" she interrupted.

"Why can't you go?"

"Because I'm a blooming teacher, that's why."

"Oh, I hadn't thought of that." Sigh! I dragged myself off to the information desk, to queue up behind the scores of keen medics, only to find myself completely on my own apart from the very relieved and grateful receptionist. A young sailor escorted me down to the medical room somewhere in the bowels of the ship to be introduced to a very anxious couple in their late 30s and thankfully English, as my foreign language skills are pretty sketchy. "Hi, I'm Doctor Brooks, a GP from Brighton. Just to let you know, I have been up most of the night driving back from the French Alps with my family and have thoroughly enjoyed a boozy lunch, so I'm not in such a great shape to start practicing medicine, but apparently, I'm the only doctor on the ship, so I'm all you have got I'm afraid." They seemed happy enough to see anyone. The patient, Theo, was already sitting up on the examination couch. "And what do you guys do for a living?" I enquired chattily.

"We are both litigation barristers." This caught my attention. "And I specialise in medical negligence," added Theo, rather apologetically. I was now completely fresh and sober as I could see myself being hauled up to the courts if I didn't get this right. Their story was that they had both been working extremely hard, (probably trying to ruin some poor GP's career because of a minor human mishap!) and had come over to Dieppe for a much-needed short break. The in-laws were looking after their three children in Hampstead. They hadn't had much sex recently and had made up for this over the weekend resulting in poor old Theo developing some chest pain and tightness during the height of passion. The medical room provided a stethoscope and blood pressure machine, so I was able to do a half-decent examination; after a tortuous hour, I felt reasonably happy that this was muscular strain rather than cardiac. I recommended that they refrained from sex on the ferry and told them to report back to their GP in the morning.

"Where have you been?" asked my wife when I eventually located them relaxing in their seats.

"You've been to the bar, haven't you Dad?" smirked my youngest. They wouldn't believe me if I told them, so I didn't.

Dr D – MARTHA'S MAGIC

As the incoming partner, I took on most of the new patients leaving Arthur Tabor (AT), with a mainly older group that included some senior civil servants, retired officers from all the armed forces and a few colonial civil servants and diplomats. The owner of a local nursing home to which we had both on occasions admitted our patients planned to start a new business, running an upmarket care home. We took on a sort of advisory role as he progressed from buying a large house on Surrenden Road to appointing staff and deciding exactly what level of care his guests would and should expect to receive.

As the development progressed and we could see that the rooms were very comfortable and attractive, we both earmarked patients who would be suitable residents. In due course, they moved in, bringing their clothes, favourite pieces of furniture, pictures and, in some cases, a spouse. They were very well looked after in what was, to all intents and purposes, a very comfortable boutique hotel with personal care, as required, provided by competent staff under the supervision of the matron, Martha.

The residents were so well cared for that vacancies were infrequent, and a long waiting list developed of people, mainly from our practice.

Deaths did of course occur, and the excellent care continued post-mortem.

I arrived one morning to confirm a death and provide the Death Certificate after a patient of mine had died, as expected, during the night.

I was surprised to find my patient looking remarkably healthy, for a corpse, fully dressed in suit and tie and sitting up on his bed with his diary in one hand and his fountain pen in the other as though poised to make an entry. I was so amazed that I thought I must have been called to someone else, and even asked how he was feeling before I could conclude that his days as a diarist were over. It was clearly the work of Matron, who must have spent a long time dressing him so carefully and applying make-up.

As Martha's efforts to present her deceased patients looking as lifelike as possible not only continued, but became ever more dramatic, I would compete to be the certifying doctor. We were called to see a deceased general who appeared to be studying a map of Egypt; a retired colonial judge who had returned to England 10 years earlier, having spent 30 years in Ceylon, wearing a lightweight tropical suit and sporting an impressive suntan; and, among many others, a local solicitor who, having been merely a lover of classical music, was now wearing white tie and tails, holding a conductor's baton and sitting in front of a music stand displaying the score of a Beethoven symphony.

A patient of mine recounted a similar experience following the death of one of the older generations of his family in his hometown of Leeds, all of whom died within about a year of each other. He found himself regularly taking the afternoon train to

Leeds, staying in The Station Hotel, and attending the funeral the following day. Saddened by the death of his favourite uncle and knowing how distressed his widowed aunt would be, he decided to pay her a visit before he sat down to enjoy his dinner at the hotel. He hadn't told his aunt of his intended visit and she was surprised and delighted to see him. He expressed his sorrow, and she related the details of the uncle's final illness. He wasn't expecting her next sentence.

"Jim, would you like to see him?" she asked, "He's in the front room."

Sure, enough Uncle Ted was in the front room, in his coffin and neatly dressed in what was probably his only suit and tie.

Still a bit shocked by this turn of events, unable to think of a suitable remark and with the silence becoming a bit oppressive he finally commented on how well the old boy looked.

"He damned well should," came the reply, "he's just had two weeks' holiday in Skegness."

Dr R – DAYS TO CELEBRATE

When I was a lot younger, I wasn't one to celebrate my birthday much. I never seemed to have the time nor inclination. Now that I am in my twilight years, my wife and I make a big effort to make each anniversary as special and memorable as we can, often planning the event well in advance. Well, this is now and that was then. Then being sometime in the 80s. I was 30-something, and on my birthday, I was rushing back to the practice for my afternoon surgery. I was running late as usual and there were already four disgruntled patients waiting outside my surgery door. "Good afternoon, everyone, I won't be a minute, sorry I am late, but I was called out to an emergency." This was my standard lie as nobody, including the staff could disprove it. However, occasionally it was true, and it used to muck up the whole day. Outside of family, nobody had mentioned my birthday, so it was a bit of a shock when I entered my consulting rooms. Hanging from the ceiling were tens of balloons of various colours gently swaying in the breeze from the open window. However, on closer inspection these were not your standard balloons but inflated condoms. I had never actually seen an inflated condom before but just hoped these were unused and not second-hand! The pharmaceutical reps used to offload samples to the family planning clinic so I assume the staff must have raided their supplies – otherwise it would have cost them a fortune. I have to say I was touched to think that my devoted staff had gone to all this trouble and was reluctant to destroy them. However, I did by bursting them all with a syringe needle, as this was the quickest way to start my surgery. For anyone who doesn't know, burst inflated condoms make a huge bang when you prick them. I imagine that 50 odd consecutive explosions must have somewhat startled the patients outside. None enquired when I eventually saw them. Three hours later, when I was packing up to go home, I noticed that I had failed to pop one of the condoms. This was bright pink in colour and was suspended from the ceiling just behind my right ear when I was positioned in the chair. Clearly not one of my patients had thought it necessary to inform me but I bet they all told the story when they got home later. All the staff, right down to the last man and woman, fervently denied that they had had anything to do with it, saying that they had better things to do with their precious time. I have never known such a bunch of liars in my life!

I have never really been one for Valentine's Day. After years of disappointments, I decided that the whole concept was ridiculous. I certainly wasn't going to waste money on overpriced cards for women who didn't appreciate them. Most blokes, I suspect, lied about the large numbers they received every year but were very reluctant to show any evidence of this apparent adulation. I am quite certain one of my needy friends buys and sends himself at least half a dozen cards each year! He even goes to the extent of driving around Sussex on his half day posting his forgeries in various post offices, then displays them in prominent positions in his surgery for at least three weeks. (Yes, he is a colleague!) How pathetic is that? Well, this all changed in 1985; February 14th arrived and with it, among my usual mountainous pile of hospital letters and junk mail, were six handwritten envelopes all with very obviously different handwriting. I wasn't too bothered and waded through the post leaving these half dozen anonymous letters to the last. My curiosity eventually came to a head, and much to my utter astonishment, each envelope contained a distinctly different Valentine card. The envelopes showed evidence of being posted from various towns, half of which I had never heard of. One was even from the Isle of Wight and another from Sark in the Channel Islands. 'Blimey,' I thought, at last women had come to their senses and were able to express their inner desires. I must admit I felt it only respectful to rearrange my office desk to accommodate these lovely cards. I spent a large part of the morning winking at all the receptionists, as I was pretty sure one or two of them had been harbouring lustful thoughts about me. It wasn't for some weeks that I eventually found out that all of them originated from a single source, a patient who had moved away several months earlier. I must admit I was a little disappointed that I only had one admirer. I was determined to get my revenge and married her some 29 years later! During that time, I continued to receive a total of zero Valentine cards, not that I was particularly bothered.

Dr D – THE HAZARDS OF DOMESTIC VISITS

For some years I was a trustee of a small charity founded by a friend, an orthopaedic surgeon, who was keen to support the training of all medical personnel involved in orthopaedic surgery. A few years ago, my friend stepped down as Chair in favour of a younger colleague and I felt that the time had come to replace me on the Board with a GP more in touch with the current medical scene. The new chair was very resistant to my retiring which, at first, I found flattering but only until he made the extraordinary statement that after working at the Royal Sussex County Hospital for eight years, I was the only GP he had ever met.

This polarisation of the medical profession into exclusively hospital or community-based practitioners is relatively new. As a junior hospital doctor working in Brighton, I met those GPs who visited their patients in hospital and attended post-graduate courses. It was customary to be invited by one's bosses to have dinner in their homes at the end of the six months spent looking after their patients and we all met at rather grand black tie BMA dinners in the wonderful Banqueting Room in the Brighton Pavilion.

Knowing each other made it easier for a GP to ask a consultant, directly, for help with a patient who was ill but whose admission to hospital might be avoidable. This very valuable support was usually just a phone conversation leading to an early out-patient appointment, but consultants were sometimes asked to visit patients in their home, which was called a DV (Domestic Visit).

A GP friend left a message requesting a DV with a nurse in the theatre where the consultant surgeon was finishing a long operating list. These operating sessions often went on long into the evening and only ended with the stitching of the incision of the last patient on the list, usually by the dogsbody houseman. My friend was surprised at not being contacted with the outcome of the consultant's visit and phoned again the next morning.

"Yes, I saw your man last night: bit of a worrier, but he seems fine. Sorry, I should have phoned you," said the surgeon.

"Were you able to examine him?"

"Yes, we had a long conversation about his symptoms, and I examined his chest and abdomen and did a PR (rectal examination): all absolutely normal."

"But he is deeply jaundiced," said the confused GP before a brief silence during which it dawned on both doctors that a deeply jaundiced man was still waiting for a visit and had a hypochondriac neighbour who couldn't believe his good luck.

I'm not sure if this service is even available to GPs today, when most patients whose symptoms may or may not require attention tend to make their way to A&E by one route or another.

Dr R – PHOTOGRAPHIC MEMORY

I had lost touch with all my friends at grammar school so it was with great pleasure that I bumped into one friend (I will call him David), on the beach on one of my few days off. David had left my school at the age of 15, without any qualifications whatsoever. He had joined his father in the rag trade and built up a large portfolio of properties in Sussex that he could quite comfortably live off. Quite a success story. However, he seemed genuinely proud of my achievements and enquired as to how difficult all the necessary studying was. Being mildly dyslexic and finding hitting the books extremely challenging I replied that, "as I had a photographic memory, I could scan a medical page in 10-15 seconds and retain all the knowledge without any effort!" I wish. The irony of my reply was completely lost on David, and I felt it insensitive of me to put him right. I was sure that, at some stage, he'd know I was pulling his leg. Some 40 years later, after I retired from medicine I bumped into David on the same beach. After a bit of catching up, he reminded me of our "photographic memory conversation" and said he had regularly dined out on the story over the years. I felt that I had to enlighten him and now I dine out on "the misunderstanding".

I still saw David from time to time, but he now seemed reluctant to engage me in any sort of conversation. However, my gifted memory did let me down somewhat when I was called to the Court as an expert witness. The case involved a punch-up outside a pub; one of participants had been a young man with an epileptic condition. This involved me being paid to sit behind the defending barrister for five days in one of Sussex's County Courts. I thought this would be a relaxing change from the relentless intensity of General Practice. In my mind, this was going to be an exciting, interesting, and fairly glamorous way of spending a week. It turned out to be extremely tedious and I found myself indulging in the odd, if not very frequent, occasional catnap. Towards the end of a long soporific afternoon on the last day, I was handed a piece of paper on which was scribbled, "Where is the scaphoid bone on the human skeleton?" Well, this got the old adrenaline circulating but my brain reacted with a complete and utter mental block (and this was pre-mobile phone and Google). I prided myself on a pretty good knowledge of the human anatomy as a result of the long hours and late nights studying, but my memory completely deserted me. The counsel clearly needed an answer quickly and, after all, I was the "expert witness". I gave it my best shot, wrote down my answer and handed back the piece of paper. Almost immediately the barrister was on his feet announcing with great gravity that, "I have it on good authority (me!), that the scaphoid bone lies in the shoulder." This seemed not to be challenged so I sat back smugly glowing in my success. The young man got off, so there was a celebration in the pub afterwards. "Well done old chap, announced the barrister, that was a great help, and I think you made a difference to the outcome of the case." "Oh, I'm only glad to be of some assistance."

When I got home, I had a quick check in my anatomy bible only to be aghast to see that the scaphoid bone had been moved from the shoulder to the wrist. However, there was a "scapular" bone in the shoulder so I can only assume that the learned lawyer was guilty of a minor spelling error. The young man in the dock seemed a nice chap so I felt justice had been done. However, I never volunteered to be an expert witness again; I was too busy pursuing other challenges.

Dr D – MALAPROPISMS

I have always taken a snide delight in other people's malapropisms and can still remember my favourites. A 60-year-old man who followed his father into a prestigious Army regiment was devastated when he developed diabetes and was deemed unfit for military service. He later developed quite severe hypertension, which I treated, and he bought one of the early home monitoring devices. Every three months he came to see me, in cavalry twill trousers, highly polished brown shoes, Viyella shirt, regimental tie, and tweed jacket, whatever the weather, to discuss his blood pressure recordings.

"Pretty happy about the systolic pressure Doc but not so sure about the apostolic."

I simply cannot resist reacting, I know it is childish, but I can't help it, and heard myself replying that I didn't think he needed to worry about the spiritual aspect of his problem, but that the lower (diastolic) figures looked fine, and he should stick with the medication, but there was no harm in prayer. He looked a bit confused but accepted my advice.

With a straight face, I responded to a patient who said he was "costive" and needed "an aperitif", with a prescription for an orange flavoured aperient which I suggested he should take half an hour before supper, in a wine glass containing "two ice cubes and a glace cherry". It was a highly successful treatment.

A large lady with arthritic knees fell over when the bus she was boarding set off a bit too rapidly. "This fall has really "exasperated her condition," her husband told me later.

This couple lived in Harewood Court, a retirement home for elderly Masons. It is a large brick building with four wings surrounding a central garden in Wilbury Road, less than 100 yards from the building in which I set up shop on my own in 1985. The residents, of whom there were about 100 when I first took over their medical care, were expertly looked after by a matron whose job was mainly administrative and two very capable nurses who lived in. No cars were allowed in the early days, the flats had no telephone and, once they moved in, their savings and pension income became the property of the Royal Masonic Benevolent Institution in return for a promise of care until they died.

Eventually the RMBI reacted to pressure from the residents and their families and installed telephones in every flat. On the first day the system became operational, one old lady, a widow who had been her dentist husband's nurse, was thrilled when her phone rang just after lunch.

On the other end, a creepy male voice asked if she was masturbating.

"Oh no, "she replied cheerily. "Thank you for asking but I finished eating an hour ago."

One morning toward the end of my first year in General Practice, there was an item on the Today programme suggesting, quite correctly in my case, that GPs were completely incompetent in the area of women's sexual health. I immediately resolved to ask any woman presenting any symptoms between knees and navel if she had any sexual problems she would like to discuss. I knew I was out of my depth but fortunately all the women to whom I made my offer declined in a "certainly not" sort of voice until I encountered Mrs V. This worn out looking 35-year-old French lady was married to a small Irishman who worked for the council. They had three children. In cowardly fashion, I suggested she might like to come and discuss her problem before the afternoon surgery, thereby giving myself time to think about how I would conduct the interview.

She turned up looking absolutely stunning. In a delightful French accent, she told me that although she and her husband had sex fairly regularly, she couldn't remember the last time she had had a climax. So far so good, I began to feel less anxious.

"All my friends zey are 'aving 'organisms' but moi, I 'ave none."

Those two little extra letters almost brought the tears of suppressed laughter to my eyes but after a brief and unnecessary trip to the examination, room I regained control and we then had a 10-minute discussion about her organisms, which she seemed to find helpful. It certainly helped me.

Dr R – THANK YOU

Mrs Kasparis suffered from a long-standing chronic anxiety/depression condition about which I used to see her every month, for general support. After a year or so, she started to bring me in a bottle or two of Liebfraumilch wine that unfortunately neither I, nor any of my family were keen on. Without wanting to seem insensitive and also because I was running out of storage space at home, I hinted that my favourite wine was Chenin Blanc and that it was a little cheaper than her Liebfraumilch.

"No problem, Doctor," said Mrs Kasparis. The following month I had rigged up an audio teaching session for a presentation at a large training afternoon at Guy's Hospital later that week. Mrs Kasparis arrived on cue with a six-pack of the preferred wine in a bottle bag. The consultation went well, I thought, but I didn't have time, or most likely forgot, to check the audio before my presentation to some 50 keen (and too politically correct for my liking) GPs.

The clinking of bottles seemed to dominate the first couple of minutes of the audio recording. You would have thought she had carried in a whole crate of wine with her – I wish. Maybe at Christmas. Mrs Kasparis greeted me with, "I bought in the wine you asked for Doctor." This got a laugh though, albeit at my expense. However, I didn't seem to impress the visiting Professor from the Royal College of Practitioners. Some of these medics are so blooming serious.

Jane Jones, a single lady of 64 who lived alone, who I had never met before, came to see me one February morning. It had been snowing and she had done well to make the surgery appointment as she lived halfway up the steepest hill in Brighton, and she arrived breathless. The physical examination was negative except that she was extremely pale. I took some blood for urgent tests and sent her home to rest, saying that I would contact her with the results. She had no landline and mobile phones had hardly been invented. (Those that were, were only suitable for weightlifters!) I told her that I would visit her later and reassured her that this was not a problem. I took the blood samples to the hospital personally, as the snow had delayed the pick-up service. That afternoon, the pathology laboratory rang to confirm that Miss Jones was severely anaemic and almost certainly due to pernicious anaemia*. Consequently, she needed to be in hospital for urgent treatment. By the end of the surgery, the snow was thick on the roads and not many vehicles had ventured out. There wasn't a bus or taxi in sight. Fortunately, I had a four-wheel drive and had little trouble climbing the steep hill to Miss Jones. There was no reply to her doorbell, but the back door was unlocked. Being the son of a police officer, and a doctor, I felt I had the right to enter her private home without invitation. (I'm not sure if that would stand up in court?) I found her fast asleep in bed. For one moment, I thought she was dead, which would have provoked the question, "Why hadn't I sent her straight to hospital in the first place?" She was happy to be admitted to hospital for treatment when I explained to her the options and what "pernicious" actually meant. The ambulance service was stretched that evening because of the heavy snowfalls, and they had doubts whether their vehicles would be able to climb the particularly steep hill where the patient lived. The only sensible alternative was to take her myself, which wasn't as easy as I had first imagined. But we both managed, and I finally got home. About four weeks later, Miss Jones came to see me. She was bright, alert and with rosy cheeks. What a success, I thought, patting myself on the back and waiting to receive further congratulations from the patient. However, neither praise nor gratitude was forthcoming, nor was she particularly friendly. It was as if we had never met. I gave her a prescription of painkillers for her osteoarthritis and off she went. I spent the next couple of minutes looking through Miss Jones's notes to update myself on her treatment. It turned out that Miss Jones was Miss Joan Jones, not Miss June Jones, and that they were identical twins. You cannot make it up, can you!

---

*Pernicious anaemia is a disease in which not enough red blood cells are produced due to a deficiency of vitamin B12. Prior to intramuscular replacements, the unfortunate patient was subjected to copious amounts of raw liver, which is apparently a rich source of the missing ingredient.

Dr D – FRIGHTENED FREDDIE

A more charitable assessor of Mr Black than me might have classed him as a rough diamond, but he was in truth a foul-mouthed bully and a domestic tyrant.

There was a discernible pattern to the timing of requests for home visits. Most were received during the morning but there was a bulge at about 5.30 when husbands like Mr B returned home to a worried wife, who had been caring for an unhappy child, and unhesitatingly undermined this long-suffering woman with the advice to "call the effing doctor, you stupid cow" or words to that effect.

My first visit to the Black household was on an overcast summer day. The house was immaculate; whatever his other failings, Mr B had made a fine job of modernising and decorating their home. Unlike their neighbours, it boasted an attractive conservatory in which, lying on the banquette sobbing, was their younger son, six-year-old Freddie,

"He's been like this since they got back from school, and he won't tell me what's wrong," said the tearful Mrs B. This prompted Mr B to get hold of Freddie's collar and give him a powerful shake while suggesting he'd better talk to me if he wanted to avoid a good hiding.

In front of the parents, I carefully examined Freddie, who

remained mute. I could find nothing wrong with him so I asked the parents if they would mind leaving the room so that I could talk privately to their miserable child. With some reluctance, they complied with my request.

Freddie was now sitting up and facing me but kept looking over his shoulder at the sky while we had a halting conversation about his day so far. At last, I said, "Freddie there must be something wrong, is something frightening you?"

"Yes," whispered Freddie, "Joey says he's going to bash my head in if it rains."

I had a related experience about 10 years later, but in very different surroundings. My practice received a small retainer from the Grand Hotel, in return for which we offered to respond to requests to see their guests, usually in the hotel. At the end of an afternoon surgery in 1983, I was asked to visit an elderly American lady who was unrousable. This was a couple of years before the Brighton Bombing but the suite I was to visit might well have been the one later occupied by Mrs Thatcher.

The noise of a party drowned my knocking, so I let myself in and was confronted by a drinks party in full swing. I recognised a few actors resident in Brighton. I was eventually approached by a 40-year-old man in a 3-piece tweed suit who greeted me rather condescendingly. I got the impression he was hoping to have summoned a more senior member of the medical profession to attend to his employer who, he told me, in a camp mid Atlantic accent, a cross between David Niven and Burt Lancaster, was none other than Miss Ida Claire.

You have probably never heard of this lady, and I certainly hadn't, but I did my best not to display my ignorance. Later, I had the chance to do some research and discovered that she had been a major silent screen star who had succeeded in continuing her career on the stage and in "talkies".

"We think she's had a stroke, poor dear."

You learn early on in a medical career never to accept other people's diagnoses, especially when presented by men with dodgy accents or wearing a bow tie.

So, we left the party, and I was shown into a long narrow room containing a single bed on which there was the motionless figure of an old but still rather beautiful lady. There were certainly no signs of her having had a stroke. In fact, there was no sign of any problem except that her eyes remained closed, and she did not respond to my questions. Having, with some difficulty, got rid of the other diagnostician in the room, I leaned over the patient and suggested tactfully that I thought I understood the situation and if she preferred to escape from the party, I would simply explain that she needed rest after her long journey.

One eye opened and in a strong voice, she said, "I wish they'd all FUCK off!" The eye closed and she went back to "sleep".

Dr R – ONLY HUMAN

I hate to think I was judged to be unprofessional or indiscreet when I was a GP, but there were times when it could all become a bit tricky. It's obvious that parts of the job were more enjoyable than others. As a practicing heterosexual, I must admit I preferred examining the female breast to inserting my fingers up some poor guy's bum in search of a rectal cancer or enlarged prostate. I always had the fear that the protective glove would split, with unpleasant consequences. When it came to examining the rest of the body (excluding female pelvic examination), rubber protection was not required. I remember with tremendous embarrassment when I was performing a routine medical on a twenty-something young woman for an insurance policy. She was extraordinarily beautiful and, while I was listening to her chest with my stethoscope, I inadvertently said, "big breasts" instead of "big breaths." The patient simply replied, "Thank you", and nothing more was said. Needless to say, she passed the medical with flying colours.

When I was quite a young GP, I had a lovely patient named Katie. She would often come to see me in the surgery complaining of a sore throat. When I offered to examine her, she would immediately strip to the waist in front of me. "Would you check my breasts while I'm here please Doctor as you know I worry about lumps." "Sure Katie, pop up on the couch then." As her mother had died of breast cancer a few years earlier, she was terrified she was doomed to the same fate. Katie, as it happened, was blessed with the most wonderful breasts, so it was no hardship for me, from time to time, to put her mind at rest. However, in a moment in which I can only describe as madness, I casually remarked that I thought she had the best breasts in the practice. She was particularly agitated that day, and I imagined it would be a kind thing to say. She thought so too, and sat up on the examination couch and said, "Oh, thank you Doctor" and gave me a big hug. I kept my hands firmly behind my back. There were no chaperones in those days. To compound my awkwardness one of the receptionists brought in a cup of tea. "Everything alright, Doctor Brooks?"

Donna joined the practice as a Junior Receptionist, aged 16. With blond hair down to her hips and legs up to her armpits, she seemed the obvious choice. She omitted to include on her CV that she had worked as an exotic photographic model for one of the top shelf magazines, when she was 14! Would she still have got the job if she had? I suspect so. A few weeks later, I spotted Donna sunbathing topless against the sea wall on the beach. To show off my athleticism and to be friendly, I leaped over the promenade railings to drop to her side (a six to eight-foot drop!) However, it didn't turn out to be Donna after all and, to make things worse, I caught my knee on the metal top of the railings, giving me excruciating pain and leaving me speechless for a full minute while trying to gesticulate to explain my mistake and avoid being arrested!

Dr D – BRIEF ENCOUNTER

When Sildenafil, sold as Viagra, first became available in the UK in 1998, it could only be dispensed by a private prescription, something many NHS GPs were entitled but loath to do.

During the following few months a number of middle aged men who had rarely, if ever, consulted me before, came to discuss vague symptoms until, often with one hand on the door handle, they would ask "Do you know anything about this Viagra stuff?"

I knew quite a lot about it, and the similar drugs that competing pharmaceutical companies had rushed to market, so I would launch into a well-practised spiel about the three available products and how they differed.

As they were all in tablet form, the rate at which they were absorbed from the stomach was influenced by the presence of food and alcohol so the speed of onset varied; also, their side effects were all slightly different as was the duration of their effectiveness.

One man started to look a bit uncomfortable as I explained that one product that was the most rapidly effective lasted for about 8 hours the next for at least 12 and the latest incarnation could be effective for up to 36 hours.

"Is there anything a bit, er shorter?" He asked.

"Why would you want that?" I responded.

"Well," he said rather sadly, "I really only need a couple of minutes."

Dr R – GAVISCON

During a rather relaxed surgery, a middle-aged man named Jim came to see me complaining of feeling low. Three months earlier, he had lost his wife, also a patient, to breast cancer. They had two children, Roy and Richard, both in their 20s and married. Unfortunately for the family, both these young men had emigrated with their wives to seek their fortunes. One had settled in New Zealand and the other in North America. Jim was not a wealthy man, so he did not have the funds to fly halfway around the world to see them. He felt isolated and very lonely. His workplace was becoming tedious, and he couldn't see any future. He began to alarm me regarding his personal safety. Fortunately, I was able to give him almost 40 minutes of my time; I felt my other patients would just have to wait. At the end of the consultation, I was confident that I could help him and prescribed a mild antidepressant. We had a brilliant in-house Counsellor, who was brought in to do regular evening sessions at the surgery, so I was able to fix him up to see her in the ensuing few days.

There are no free lunches with most medications, so I explained some of the common side effects of this particular drug. As I was about to take two weeks' leave, I arranged for Jim to see one of my partners for a follow-up in 7 days' time and then a week after that. Off I went on holiday and tried to forget everything that worried me in the surgery. On my return to work, the telephone rang, as the "depressed" patient was downstairs in my partner's surgery. My colleague was bemused as to why I had treated the man with an antacid! I too was lost for an explanation. However, Jim, now apparently fully recovered, was so grateful to me that he had brought in a couple of bottles of wine to thank me. We agreed that he could probably come off his very "helpful medication" and to seal an unwritten non-disclosure agreement I donated, one of the bottles to my partner albeit reluctantly.

I seem to have a thing about this particular antacid, Gaviscon, as years later, after I had retired and was on holiday in Menorca, I developed "heartburn" after lunch. A quarter of an hour of pouring copious amounts of the magic liquid down my throat proved unsuccessful, as it turned out to be a heart attack! At least I got the diagnosis half-correct. I was flown over to Majorca, where they popped a stent into the offending coronary artery and here, I am today, 14 years later. Thirty minutes of chest pain, unrelieved by half a bottle of Gaviscon, should be taken seriously. I don't recommend this pathway to a diagnosis, as not everyone survives the first half hour!

On the same subject, Dr Douglas Chamberlain was a completely dedicated National Health Service Consultant Cardiologist (no private patients), who worked principally at the Royal Sussex County Hospital in Brighton. He realised that, if treatment could be initiated within the first hour of a heart attack, the survival rates were much higher. With this in mind, he trained up appropriate ambulance men and women with the correct tools (portable ECG machines etc) and the permission to treat (morphine and 'clot busting' medication). This model was rolled out in East Sussex, with great success. There was always at least one "Cardiac Ambulance" on duty at any one time. This program was in full flow in East Sussex as far back as the mid-1970s. My heart attack happened in 2008, some 30 years later. I had been windsurfing all day, in Menorca. The Tramontana wind was in full power, and none of us wanted to miss it. Once it had blown through, the wind could disappear for a frustrating week. When I realised this chest pain wasn't going to go away and remembered that my father had died of a myocardial infarct at the age of 60 (I was just 61), I asked the staff in the hotel for assistance. I didn't feel well enough to accept a lift to the main hospital, in Mahon, so they called an ambulance. Within 15 minutes, two English-speaking Spanish ambulance people were in my hotel room, a cardiac male doctor, and a cardiac female nurse. I had used these precious few minutes waiting by gathering up useful items to take to the hospital: money, credit cards, mobile phone (though I forgot the blooming charger) and the vital European Health Insurance Card. Most importantly of all I crawled to my suitcase and fished out a fresh pair of underpants. My mother had impressed upon me as a child to always wear clean underwear, in case I was ever involved in an accident and needed to go to hospital. Now, 57 years later, that advice was finally bearing fruit. My room was on the first floor, and a flight of stairs needed to be negotiated. When they sat me up in a chair, I nearly fainted so they took me down the stairs on a stretcher in the horizontal position, no mean task. At the left-hand turn, halfway down the flight of stairs, there was a large mirror. I remember looking up and adjusting my hair so that I could look my best for the hospital. I think I was brought up to maintain standards at any cost, no matter what the crisis was. Unbeknownst to me at the time, I had suffered a cardiac arrest in the ambulance and been resuscitated; the same happened again soon after reaching Casualty (so that was two of my nine lives used up already). One great comfort to me was that throughout this dramatic episode in my life, one of the female windsurfing instructors, Fiona, held my hand without saying anything. With her other hand she wrote messages to four of the most important people in my life at the time in case something happened to me, like dropping dead, for example. They were to my second wife, Rachel, and our beloved son Freddie, Louise, my girlfriend, who I married soon afterwards, and my best friend, who I have since fallen out with. Thankfully, these messages were not delivered; clearly, I survived. I was flown over to the cardiac centre in Palma, Majorca, with my own personal pilot (obviously) and an accompanying medic in case I arrested again. An angiogram showed a block in one of my coronary arteries. A stent was successfully manoeuvred into position, and I was able to watch the whole painless procedure on the monitor screen without the least anxiety. It is amazing what a drop of morphine can do. Two days later, I was transferred from the intensive cardiac unit into a general medical ward. While they were transferring me from the trolley on to my bed, I apparently arrested twice and needed to be "shocked" to get me going again, (that's four lives gone, only five left!) I woke up to find a crowd of medics around me, and Louise in the background. She had flown over from England that morning. I proposed to her a little later when it had all quieted down a bit; she accepted and offered to move in with me when we arrived back in Brighton, until I got better. To be honest, I haven't felt 100% since, and so she has been living here some 14 years now!

One of the problems with morphine and most painkillers is that they constipate the hell out of you. I hadn't had a "poo" for 10 days which was my record to date, and I have no intention of trying to beat it. Louise popped out for a large bottle of a liquid laxative. She was gone a long time as her Spanish isn't great. I was in a cosy side ward with three other noisy Spanish patients, along with their wives, children, grandchildren, and grandparents. Thankfully, animals were not allowed in the hospital. Why they had to have the TV on so loud was beyond me. I thought they were supposed to be ill too. We all shared one bathroom and toilet and, as I knew that I might require its services for some time, maybe hours, I used the general ward's bank of WC's. Sure, enough I was gone a long time, but it was worth it. The downside for the hospital, however, was that I passed so many "rocks" that the Spanish plumbing couldn't cope with it! If anyone had the unkindness to say, "That Rod Brooks is full of shit," well, every seven days I guess they would have been right. I arrived back in the UK several pounds lighter, hanging onto my bursting catheter bag that I had forgotten to empty on the plane. The removal of my catheter would have to wait for another day.

Several years later, now married to Louise, we were attending a charity curry evening. Much to my delight, Douglas Chamberlain was in attendance with his wife. Both in their 90s and looking remarkably fit. I managed to corner the great man during a break in the proceedings and said, "Dr Chamberlain, you probably don't remember me, but I did my junior house physicians' job at Brighton General Hospital and then joined the local GP Vocational Training Scheme, all back in the 1970s." He smiled a little. I said, "You saved my life." This got his attention. I went on to tell him about my cardiac experience in the Balearic Islands and how the Brighton model of ambulance intervention had probably saved my family the expense of repatriating my corpse back to the UK! Hopefully, we would have been insured for this event because I believe it can be pretty pricey. The temptation to leave the body abroad must be very attractive on some folk's budgets if they are covered by a dodgy insurance policy. He looked genuinely chuffed with my mini outburst, and I am so glad I made the effort.

Dr D – THE BELLE OF WATERLOO STREET

During the early 1970s, almost all General Practices and consultants in private practice used a 24-hour phone answering service provided by a very charming and efficient couple called Mr and Mrs Kavanagh. The two of them ran this service on their own from a small basement flat in Ditchling Road and at 6 pm on weekdays and over weekends, dozens of doctors' phone lines were diverted to their little office.

Mrs K, who was disabled and chair-bound, was, only occasionally it seemed, replaced by her husband, a genial Irishman, who sometimes did a night shift. When he had woken you in the middle of the night, he tried to soothe the irritation caused by offering a joke before giving the bad news that you had to get up and get out. There were many better than this, but this is the only one I can remember:

"What is the definition of a contraceptive, Dr Stewart?"

"OK, let's have it Mr Kavanagh."

"A contraceptive, my dear doctor is, as everybody knows, a labour-saving device to be used on every conceivable occasion."

One evening when I was doing my regular weekly night on call, I got a message to ring Mrs K, who told me I had two visits to make, one to an old bronchitic patient of mine and another to a 40-year-old patient of the other practice we covered.

"Her voice was a bit weak over the phone, but she asked who was on call and was pleased to hear it was you."

"Do you think that's a good thing?" I asked.

"I think you are soon going to find out" said the enigmatic Mrs K and rang off.

I decided to do the second call first and drove to the address in Waterloo Street. These were the days before parking restrictions, and I had no problem finding a space. Widely known as "Sin Street", Waterloo Street and the narrow roads leading off it were the closest thing Brighton had to a red-light area with at least a couple of brothels and a number of houses, like the one I found myself in front of, with rooms let to the girls "on the game".

I rang the bell labelled Simone, Flat 2, and immediately the lock buzzed, I was let in.

My patient was holding open the door of Flat 2 and I realised that I had seen her before but could not recall where or when.

She was an unusual looking woman probably just on the right side of 40. Tall and slim, she had long grey hair piled up on her head kept in place by large combs, extensive dark eye shadow, almost white face make-up and mauve lipstick that matched her nail polish. She would have passed for a Goth but for the red high-heeled patent leather shoes and the leather mini skirt. Her appearance was interesting rather than alluring, with large eyes, quite a prominent nose and what was referred to as a weak chin. I wondered briefly if she was a provider of one of the more arcane sexual services.

She motioned that I should enter. The room was quite sparsely furnished: bed, sofa, big mirror on one wall and a dressing table. No photos, pictures or ornaments and the only source of light was a flimsy looking bedside lamp.

She was clearly finding it difficult to speak but I eventually got a history of sore throat and loss of voice for 24hrs, and she thought her temperature was raised. She did have a slightly raised temperature and a very red throat. So, after a few more questions and making sure she had no antibiotic allergies I sat on an upholstered bench at the end of the bed facing away from her, made a few notes on one of the brown cards that fitted into the old Lloyd George medical record envelopes and wrote a prescription for Ampicillin.

"I'm not sleeping, Doctor," she squeaked. "Could I have a few Moggies?"

I could have refused, but I added a dozen Mogadon sleeping tablets to the script. GPs were a bit more relaxed about prescribing sedative medicines in those days.

Her voice was indistinct, and I probably wasn't listening sufficiently carefully, but I heard her say something about my being very kind and I replied that that was generous of her.

It took a few moments to pack my papers and the tools of the trade back into my case; when I turned to hand her the prescription, she had removed her skirt and blouse and was giving me a sly smile.

It wasn't exactly embarrassment I felt, it was more a sense that I had somehow misheard my way into a sort of barter arrangement, and it felt a bit ungracious to reject the offer. I think the word "in" may have preceded the word "kind".

She accepted my explanation of needing to do an urgent call with a slightly theatrical look of disappointment.

I heard myself saying, "Perhaps another time" in an attempt to moderate any feeling of rejection and headed for the door.

I didn't feel that my moral fibres had been significantly tested and simply felt rather foolish, not for the last time.

I never saw her again in a professional capacity, mine or hers, but occasionally over the next few years when out shopping with my wife or daughters she would suddenly appear by my side and, in a conspiratorial voice, would say, "I still owe you one Doctor" and then slide away.

Dr R – CATHETER STORIES

Terminal care in the community was an extremely important role in a GP's life. The aim was to keep the patient as comfortable as possible and allow the person to die in a manner that he or she wished, if possible. Obviously, there were ethical boundaries. For example, I could not accept a request for me to terminate a patient's life. I was on duty one weekend and looking after a patient named Bill, who had cancer of the lung that had spread to most parts of his body and was coming to the end of his life. He was a widower and lived with his daughter, son in law, and granddaughter. The daughter rang me to tell me that, although her father had been in a coma for the last 24 hours, he had become very restless and appeared to be in great pain. On my visit, I agreed and injected him intramuscularly with an appropriate dose of morphine. It should have had some effect within 10-20 minutes, but it didn't. I repeated the dose no less than three times, without the slightest effect on his restlessness. I needed to go to the local chemist to restock as I had used up my last dose. I called in the district nurses to make him as comfortable as possible in my absence. Half an hour later, a very experienced nurse rang me to tell me that she thought the patient had gone into urinary retention* and that his extended bladder was easily palpable in his abdomen, the size of a 20-week pregnancy. So blooming obvious really, if I had done the basics and put a hand on his tummy. All I could think of was that, if ever I was in such an awful plight, I hoped that the duty doctor was more competent than me! The level of discomfort must have been so high that large doses of morphine didn't touch the sides. The nurse agreed to catheterise* him as I was now at the other end of the city dealing with another emergency, hopefully with better results. An hour later, I returned to my patient, who was now sleeping like a baby. A guilty hand on his abdomen revealed no swelling or tenderness. This incident haunted me for my whole career in General Practice, and when I became a trainer, I used to drum into the trainees and medical students that on no account should they miss an extended bladder, as it is unforgiveable to do so. A good 25 years later, I found myself in a florist buying flowers for my wife (and no, I am not all bad!), when the woman at the counter exclaimed, "It's Doctor Brooks, isn't it?" It turned out that this was the granddaughter of the poor man I had so badly managed. I was able to tell her that his horrible pain had been due to my ineptitude, but that this awful experience had prevented countless patients in a similar situation from suffering the same fate. This brought a smile to her face. Some people are so generous. I wanted to buy her some flowers, but I was too embarrassed to do so. Unknowingly, she had closed a wound that had been open for a quarter of a century.

I never enjoyed catheterising men, and, in retrospect, I don't think I was particularly gentle when I did. I just wanted it over and done with. I personally needed catheterisations for all my neurosurgical* procedures. My very sympathetic neurosurgeon agreed to catheterise me "on the table" after I had been anaesthetised. Thank you, sir. The catheters were removed 2-3 days post-op by one of the nurses and that was bad enough. However, the last time (so far) the surgeon operated on me for a cervical disc prolapse I developed a urinary tract infection, and the tube was removed a little earlier than before. I was started on the appropriate antibiotic, but I failed to pee! "Oh no, call the duty surgeon please." It was 10pm and the ward was down to a skeleton staff. The only available medic was tied up in an emergency operation and would probably not be available for another 3-4 hours. My discomfort was bordering on agony. This seemed like God punishing me for my previous incompetence. I don't believe in God, but it didn't stop me praying for relief. Three hours' later, when I would have willingly shot myself, if I had had the means, I suddenly and inexplicably passed a "gallon" of urine. Oh, what paradise! I believed in miracles, albeit for one evening.

When I suffered my heart attack in Menorca and was flown over to Majorca for treatment, the first thing a rather austere looking female nurse wanted to do was catheterise me. I was in no situation to object and nobody appeared to speak English anyway. As it happened, I was at the time, pretty high on morphine – therapeutic, not recreational – so the experience wasn't as traumatic as I had anticipated. After the cardiac team had put in my coronary artery stent* and resuscitated me a couple of times, it was time for my catheter to be removed. Terrified of my previous experiences of post-op retention, I wouldn't allow them to take it out and successfully nursed it for the next seven days until I reached the UK, where I had pre-arranged for an anaesthetist colleague of mine to remove it. He cycled in the next day to my home, borrowed some kitchen scissors, and duly cut the tube. "Have you ever done this before, because I haven't?" I asked rather nervously. "Nope, I always get a nurse to do it for me," came the reply. Too late for a change of plan, I thought. Now this tube has two separate channels running down its length. One tube, open at both ends, drains urine into a handy collection bag. The other has a valve on the outside end – concentrate – this bit is important – this connects to a balloon at the inside tip. The balloon is inflated with sterile water (but I guess Chardonnay would work just as well) when it lies inside the bladder to stop it from slipping out. My nightmare is the thought that, when the tube is cut, the balloon somehow fails to deflate. In that scenario, when the tube is given an encouraging tug, it attempts to drag the bladder into the outside world. I have never heard of this happening but there is always a first time and that could be me! But it wasn't. However, I still needed to pee unaided which I did an hour later. It was a lovely sunny morning to complement my mood. My wife, Louise, and I went for a walk along Brighton promenade, but my feet didn't touch the ground.

*Urinary retention: failure to pass urine. Medicine is not that difficult to understand really, it's just that doctors need to mystify it to justify our salaries.

*Catheterisation is commonly performed with a Foley Catheter (named after Frederick Foley, who produced the original design in 1929). It is a flexible tube that is passed through the urethra and into the bladder to drain urine. In males, the tube is passed through the penis and in women it is not.

*Neurosurgical procedures. Over a period of five years, I suffered four disc prolapses in my "neck-spine" and one in my chest spine, all of which needed to be fixed

*A coronary stent is a tube-shaped device placed in the coronary arteries that supply blood to the heart, to keep the arteries open in the treatment of coronary heart disease.

Dr D – THE PLACEBO QUEEN

My great great grandfather was a 14-year-old cabin boy on a Newcastle coal boat when, in 1804, it was captured by a French frigate just off the coast at Brighton. He spent the next eight years in France as a prisoner of war, often being marched barefoot across the country with a chain round his neck. It was a very rough upbringing and he quickly learned how to defend himself. One of his grandchildren, my grandfather (born in 1872), had a much gentler upbringing and was a talented all-round sportsman and a competent boxer. One of the partners in his medical practice in Barnet came to work one day in a clearly inebriated state. He was warned by my grandfather that he would "lay him out" if he ever did so again. The hapless doctor did not heed the warning and a few days later was pulled into the dispensary by my irate grandfather, knocked out and then kicked out, never to return. No messing around with Human Resources in those days.

During calmer times in the dispensary, my grandmother concocted coloured liquids with assorted flavours, which her husband prescribed as tonics, medicines for particular symptoms and restoratives. The bottles were all neatly labelled and sealed with wax; they contained not a single active ingredient. Time was relied upon to solve most minor medical problems and a spoonful of purple medicine taken three times a day after meals reminded the patient that they had successfully transferred responsibility for their wellbeing to their doctor, who would see them again in the unlikely event of their symptoms persisting.

Placebos were still an important part of the GP's therapeutic armoury when I went into practice, until sadly everyone was made aware that they were being duped. The placebos had often been very effective and totally safe. Even today the penicillin prescribed for a virus infection, on which it can have no effect, is by way of example, simply a more sophisticated, and potentially more dangerous, version of the same medical response. It gets someone out of the patients' chair.

Many years ago, the building on the Brighton seafront immediately west of the Grand Hotel, now The Empress Suite, housed a rest home called Grosvenor House whose 30 or so residents were carefully and wisely looked after by Miss Withers, the matron. This adorable woman was in her 70s, and about five feet tall; she spoke with an Anglo-Indian lilt to her voice and managed the difficult feat of being authoritative without being the least bit unfriendly; her residents loved her. I don't know for certain if she had any formal nursing training, but she unfailingly recognised significant symptoms and, when required to treat the "well but worried" residents, she proved herself a placebo prescriber of genius.

Her system of dispensing reassurance, reinforced by innocuous treatments, started with a small plain white tablet containing a very small dose of vitamin C. The patient was told exactly when to take the pill and received a stern warning about the dangers of exceeding the daily dose. If this failed, the patient received an effervescent version of the same preparation. Next came a green multivitamin liquid decanted into a brown glass bottle labelled "The Mixture." If the symptoms persisted or were worsening, they next received an intramuscular injection of a minute amount of sterile water and were put on the list to be seen by me at the weekly surgery. Her final treatment, reserved for patients with only the most persistent anxiety was an injection of Vitamin B12. This bright pink liquid came in small glass phials, and no one had ever been known to require more than a single dose.

At some point in the early 1960s, the manager of a large seafront hotel asked me to visit the actor Richard Harris, who was doing two concerts at the Dome and staying in the hotel. His effective, but not very melodious rendition of Jimmy Webb's great song "MacArthur Park" was the highlight of the show. Someone had told him that a shot of B12 would improve his voice. Would I be willing to give him the injection? I'm just as big a sucker for celebrities as everyone else, so naturally I agreed. He was neither friendly nor grateful, but I gave the injection, pocketed the £20 offered by his gofer and left as quickly as possible. We got the same request the following day and he was equally unpleasant, which was saddening as I considered him a very fine actor and resented having my admiration tarnished.

Dr R – BLOODY HELL

For five years, I worked for the British Pregnancy Advisory Service (BPAS), which had clinics running daily in their hospital in central Brighton. I was one of the GPs who did a regular session as a counselling/assessing doctor for women who were unsure whether to continue their pregnancy. I became pretty much burnt-out with the work after year five and packed it in. I was very disheartened by the attitude of many of the so-called partners of these very distressed young ladies, and I was becoming mildly depressed and disillusioned with it all. However, I did enjoy providing vasectomy counselling sessions, explaining it was all very simple and only needed to be done under a local anaesthetic. BPAS didn't provide a follow-up clinic post-operatively, so I assumed all went well. However, when it came to my decision some years later to have the snip, I went back to my old teaching hospital, Charing Cross (as I didn't trust anyone locally) and opted for a general anaesthetic. I remember being very sick on the journey back to Brighton, and somewhat doubting my decision not to stay on home turf. It did allow me to play the hero for several days until my family got sick of hearing about it!

I also helped run an Artificial Insemination Donor/Husband (IAD/IAH) clinic at the BPAS Hospital. I used to do this in my lunch-hour, happily impregnating up to six women in a session. Straws of defrosting semen were presented to me that I then sucked up in a syringe before squirting all around the waiting cervix. The success rate was quite high, and it was extremely satisfying to be part of it all. However, it did remind me of the time when, as a poor medical student, I was approached by some firm asking if I would donate my sperm. The fee was tempting but, in the end, I declined, feeling slightly uneasy about producing children that I was never going to know about. They were looking for healthy, white, middle-class, athletic, intelligent and good-looking young men to provide the specimens – well, that was a perfect description of me – no wonder they sought me out! I did wonder at the time how easy it would be to sabotage the whole system. I had a great friend who could provide a specimen for me, the only difference between us was that he was black! The thought of an infertile member of the Royal Family receiving this sample in good faith somewhat amused me at the time. However, if this got back to me, I had visions of me floating down the Thames face down. A black future King of England! Maybe it would have been worth it.

My ex-mate George inexplicably emigrated to Canada at very short notice. There was no time for a leaving party; one minute he was here, the next he was gone. He did, to his credit, work in a garden centre in North America and eventually owned his own very successful business. He married and had a couple of kids. However, a few weeks after he left, his very beautiful girlfriend Gina, who he had dumped, turned up at one of my termination counselling sessions. "Hello Roddie," she chirped as I rushed into the clinic, late as usual. There were three doctors on duty that morning and I made it clear to the staff that I would prefer it if the other medics dealt with her. Of course, that didn't happen, so she arrived in the examination room as my second patient. Bear in mind that, when Gina had been dating George, I had quite fancied her, as had everyone I knew. Now, she was my patient, albeit for 20-30 minutes only. Much to my relief the physical examination was uneventful, mainly because she was so relaxed about it all. When it came to me taking a blood sample all went well. Having found a suitable vein in her arm, I extracted 10ml of blood into a syringe that I then squirted into a test-tube. All routine that except this test-tube had no bottom to it and the whole sample was sprayed all over my white shirt and long white coat! You have no idea how far 10mls of blood can go. I had to excuse myself and walk out into the still very full waiting room looking as if I had just murdered the patient in the room I had just left. You must remember these were anxious young ladies to start with. It turned out to be a very long morning and I have never seen Gina gain. I like to think she was better off without George, as I always thought he was a bit of a selfish shit.

I felt confident taking blood right from the start and flattered myself that I was pretty good at it. The practice nurses gradually took over this role and, on the whole, I was grateful for this. From time to time, I liked to keep my hand in. I was occasionally asked to asked do a venesection from a particularly difficult arm when nurses had already failed and wanted me to fail as well. I remember one extremely busy Monday morning. I was halfway through an endless surgery and already running half an hour late when one of our nurses rang to ask me to take blood from an eight-year-old girl, Laura, who they had bruised twice already. The mother of the child did not want to come back on another day, which was my suggestion, so I reluctantly trudged downstairs to the nurses' station. The little girl was already in tears, so it didn't look as if this was going to be an easy task. To cheer her up I breezily said, "Don't worry Laura; I know what I am doing. I saw it done on the TV last night on one of those hospital serials". I thought this was rather witty and would win her over to seeing me as someone who was completely competent. Clearly, it didn't work, as she took a swipe at me with her very long and sharp fingernails. She nearly took one of my eyes out and left a thin abrasion on my cheek, an injury that I found difficult to explain when I got home that evening. The mother was inexplicably outraged at my behaviour, scooped up her horrible little girl and marched out of the room. "Result" I thought and went back upstairs to my patients who appreciated me much more. I did wonder if there was going to be a complaint in the pipeline, but none arrived. Probably the mother came to her senses and severely reprimanded her child for her poor behaviour when they got home. More likely, the family registered with another practice; that of course was their prerogative.

Dr D – THE SHIPMAN EFFECT

Some GPs used to feel able to assist patients in extremis to have an easy death. Everything changed in 2000 with the trial and conviction of Dr Harold Shipman at Preston Crown Court. Officially, Shipman, a seemingly trusted and liked GP, murdered 15 of his patients. It is generally believed that he assisted at least 215 of them to die, but these patients had not been in extremis and did not want to be assisted to an untimely death by a dose of morphine.

Shipman's case triggered the most draconian changes in General Practice during my career. Single-handed practitioners were now pressured into joining larger group practices. Certainly, many large practices provide very good patient care, but there was an increasing retreat from the old doctor-patient relationship so that it has become harder for patients to access medical attention, which then tends to be provided by a doctor unknown to them. Sadly, the days of Dr Finlay are gone, and this impersonalised primary care is all that many people have ever experienced. Under the old system, even in the 1970s and 1980s, GPs usually had the great advantage of knowledge of their patients and their patients' family members; in turn, patients had an accessible physician, who they knew and trusted.

I accept that it is often misguided to look at the past too

uncritically. After all, Shipman was permitted by the old system. Nevertheless, I admit to an inclination to see the 70s and early 80s as a golden age of medical practice. There were, of course, many inadequacies, but something very valuable was lost as a consequence of the action of one mad member of our own profession, which had up to then regulated itself with reasonable success.

Post-Shipman, GPs have been strongly discouraged from carrying and administering injectable opiate drugs. This severely limits a doctor's ability to provide care for terminally ill patients in their own homes. To die in one's own home is something that most of us would prefer, but thanks to Shipman, this became increasingly rare. Cicely Saunders set up the first modern hospice, St Christopher's in Sydenham, in 1967, others followed and now provide exemplary care for patients at the end of their lives whether as in-patients or, following the effective exclusion of GPs, in patients' homes or Nursing Homes.

In the old days, GPs might occasionally discuss with their more trusted colleagues the challenging moral questions raised by assisting death, but after Shipman, such topics are generally taboo. Not so long ago, I experienced an exception to this code of silence.

In the early 1970s, I played tennis with Mark. Sadly, Mark's mother fell fatally ill with breast cancer. She had undergone successful surgery eight years earlier but had not been regularly followed up and had developed cancer in her other breast, which had spread widely before it was diagnosed. During the week before she died, by which time she had been treated with maximum doses of chemotherapy and radiotherapy, she was bedbound, and Mark and his siblings were summoned to their parents' house to say their goodbyes. Her GP, Dr X, who was held in high esteem by this family, had looked after them all for many years. He dealt with her final days, and she died peacefully in her own bed shortly after her children's visit.

Later I got to know Dr X well. Sadly, he himself fell fatally ill with smoking-related cancer. He did not have the chance to die at home and I visited him in his local hospice. He seemed keen to reminisce and we talked about colleagues past and present, family and mutual friends. He was slightly breathless and was sedated by the painkillers he was receiving via a syringe driver. I was keen not to tire him by staying too long.

There was a prolonged silence, and I was just about to stand up and take my leave of him, when he asked me if I still played tennis with Mark and if I had ever met his mother. I said that I did and had, and he became more animated and proceeded to tell me in detail about her death. He told me that, early in Mark's mother's final illness, it was already quite clear that she could not survive much longer. She had, he said, asked him almost casually if, when the time came, he would "help her out". Without really considering the possible implications of agreement, he instinctively promised that he would help in any way he could. On her last day, he visited her, for a second time, in the evening. Her husband was holding her hand. Her face was swollen, she was breathless and in pain whenever she tried to move, but in a surprisingly strong voice she reminded her doctor of his promise.

"Do you mean now?" he asked.

"Yes," she replied, "We have all discussed it and the family understands that I cannot go on like this – and you did promise to help me."

Dr X tried to disguise the alarm and discomfort he felt and nodded, before going back to his car to collect a syringe and ampoules of morphine. There, he discovered that there was only a single ampoule in his bag so, with embarrassment added to a mixture of other unfamiliar feelings, he explained the problem and headed for the local late-night chemist for a larger supply.

When he returned to the house, the three of them talked for a few minutes until his injection began its effect and she became comatose. He suggested to her husband that he leave the room, and a few minutes later, her breathing stopped. Having confirmed death, he and the husband sat together in mutually consoling silence.

During this story, I had begun to feel that I was witnessing a deathbed confession and, when he stopped talking, I asked him if he felt guilty about his actions. He assured me, "No, not at all, I think it was one of the most important events in my life. It might not have been legal, but I know it was the right thing to do for her. She was a brave woman."

I agree with Dr X that he had done the right and humane thing; now such courageous humanity by a GP is rarely possible and never to be confessed. I did not see him again. His pain worsened and was treated with a slightly higher dose from the syringe driver. He died a day later.

Dr R – BEST NOT TO KNOW

Amanda, a rather over-the-top, glamorous and extremely likeable 30-something came to see me for some personal advice. I was thumbing through her voluminous medical notes when I noticed she had attended the Gender Realignment Clinic, at Charing Cross Hospital where I trained. We were chatting rather loudly about old times at the Cross and exchanging stories when I stumbled on her surgical notes. I had never guessed that "Mandy" had had a sex change; previously, she had been Alan, a Metropolitan Police Inspector. Ten minutes into this revelation, she asked me to keep my voice down, as her husband, who was also a patient of mine, was waiting outside and apparently did not know about her history and previous surgery. "Wow," I thought, and then came the bombshell. She owned up to having a rather torrid affair with one of my colleagues. Well, I had a rather challenging relationship with one of my partners and I was hoping against hope that it was him. Not so. It turned out to be another patient of mine (a practicing surgeon locally) who happened to be the most egocentric, self-deluded lady-killer I had ever met. I would just love to have broken the "good news'" to him. However, my total professionalism forbade this luxury – damn it!

I nearly forgot to ask her why she had come to see me. Apparently, she felt tired for no apparent reason. Examination on the couch didn't help me with a diagnosis so I sent her downstairs to the nurses for some routine blood tests. I popped down later to see how they had got on. The first thing they said: "That was a bloke, wasn't it?" "What makes you say that?" I asked.

"It's blooming obvious Rod. Where have you been all your life?" There was no answer to that, but it did get me thinking. Perhaps her husband had also had a sex change and he was genetically a woman. I fished out his notes and was genuinely disappointed to find no evidence to prove that. By coincidence, two weeks later, my wife and I bumped into her in the high street. She was late for an appointment, so we only had a brief introduction and chat. After she scurried off my wife said, "That was a bloke wasn't it, Rod?"

I defensively asked, "Was she?" For the record, the blood test was normal, and I simply invited her to make another appointment.

Dr D – STAR TURN

One of the more memorable characters that I looked after was a man called Buster Lloyd Jones, who was a veterinary homeopath. He shared a large house overlooking the Hove Recreation Ground with a lady called Dorothy and, following the death of his partner a few years before I met him, with a younger, very affable man called Tom, who was his carer. Buster had suffered from polio as a child and was now chair-bound. He had written two volumes of autobiography, and some well received books dealing with animal welfare in general and the importance of a proper diet in particular. He strongly favoured a vegetarian diet himself and promoted this for animals where appropriate in his practice, in print and by setting up a company, Denes, to manufacture pet foods and nutritional supplements.

He was retired when I met him, but he had been an enormously popular and successful vet in his day and much admired for having adopted abandoned and injured animals, particularly during WW11. He was a handsome man and always, thanks to Tom, immaculately dressed and groomed.

He suffered from asthma and COPD (Chronic Obstructive Pulmonary Disease). He chose to avoid British winters if he could, by decamping to Los Angeles where he had a second thriving practice looking after the pets of the rich and famous, especially ex-pat British actors.

I noticed on one midday visit that the house was particularly tidy and there was what sounded like a gathering of women chatting in the sitting room. When I had finished dealing with his medical problems Buster asked if I would like to stay for a drink and meet someone famous. I refused the drink but did stay for 10 minutes, which was long enough to be introduced to the ladies I had heard earlier, and to witness the arrival of Clark Gable.

The group of ladies, who included Joan Plowright, Dora Bryan and Flora Robson were ecstatic and Mr Gable, who was not looking that well, was sat in the middle of the sofa and was subjected to a barrage of welcoming plaudits.

Buster still looked after several crippled pets, one of which was a three-legged Pug, who settled himself on the floor next to the great man's two-tone shoes and was perfectly placed for what happened next.

The star of Gone with the Wind clearly had bronchitis and gave a huge cough, which sent one of his dentures flying onto the carpet. The pug clearly thought this was the start of a game; he seized the teeth between his own and, with remarkable speed headed out through the conservatory to the compost heap with the Brighton thespians in hot pursuit. The teeth were rescued and washed, then their owner disappeared briefly into the cloakroom, reappeared smiling and ignored the whole episode. He certainly did not appear to give a damn!

Dr R – IT'S HARD NOT TO LAUGH SOMETIMES

It was 3am on a Sunday morning when the phone rang, waking me up with a start. I had been on call all weekend and I was exhausted and pretty fed up. "I can't sleep," said a rather excitable sounding young man. I knew this chap quite well and he was forever ringing at ridiculous hours with trivial ailments. I am sure that there was some deep psychological reason for his behaviour, but I did not have the skills to sort this out. Recognising my limitations, I had recently referred to him to our in-house counsellor. "That makes two of us now" I replied completely lacking in any sympathy whatsoever. Two hours later (well it felt like two hours), when I was confident that there was nothing serious going on, and he certainly didn't require a visit, I offered him a solution. "There is a 24-hour sweet shop on the High Street in Brighton, and they stock juicy fruits for patients with sleeping problems. I suggest you go there now and buy a couple of packets. Unfortunately, they are not available under the National Health Service."

"Thank you, Doctor." We said good night and he never bothered me again out of hours. I assume the treatment worked!

One day, on a particular hot August afternoon, I came across two patients who had had unpleasant experiences with flying insects. A young man had been yawning while waiting for a train to London at Brighton station. An opportunistic wasp had flown in, stung him on the tongue, and made a hasty retreat. The other unfortunate patient was a 40-something lady boasting a fashionable beehive hairstyle. Several bees had attempted to make this their new home. By the time both patients had reached me, they had recovered, but it could have been a lot worse. Why did I laugh when they told me of their traumas? Nervous relief, I expect.

Most of our patients who required oxygen at home had lung damage caused by smoking. Mrs Smith (not her real name) rang me to say that her husband had blown himself up. The story was that he had had his oxygen going full blast, but was dying for a fag, and you can guess the rest. I sent an ambulance to him as an emergency because I was fearful that this was all going to end in tears, which it did, as he died two days later in hospital. Why was it that everyone I told this story to laughed (but not me)? What I definitely didn't find funny was that he left £2,000 in cash to one of my partners in his will, and that was a lot of money 30 years ago. I wouldn't say no to it now.

Dr D – THE OLD WARRIOR

The local dermatologist, with by far the most successful private practice in Brighton, was Pat Hall Smith; his advice to anyone contemplating trying to attract private work was the Three A's; 'Ability, Affability and Availability', of which he considered the last the most important and I think he was probably correct. We did our best to accommodate our patients and I instructed every new receptionist to fit in any patient who wanted to be seen, NHS or private, at the end of my surgery. This did not often require me to do a significantly longer working day and we never had to deal with complaints about unavailability.

Four GPs worked a rota for out-of-hours work, which meant being on call one night a week and for one weekend a month, which included a Saturday morning surgery. This was not usually fully booked which gave time to do some paperwork.

One Saturday morning, I answered the phone to a member of the House of Lords, who wished me to inform "the good doctor Tabor, that one has a son."

Half an hour later, another patient I had not met before phoned to say that he was experiencing "a haemorrhage from me ear" and was coming straight around.

My room was at the end of a corridor leading from the front door, which I could see from my chair; 10 minutes later a tall, stooped man of about 85 was marching towards me.

"You must be Stewart." I agreed and he introduced himself as "Colonel Jones."

He struggled out of a heavy black overcoat which I hung on the back of the door while he eased himself with obvious difficulty into the patients' chair. He was a handsome old boy with strong features, a large aquiline nose and a full head of white hair that was partly obscured by the layers of pink loo paper wrapped round his head and covering both ears.

The bleeding appeared to have begun spontaneously; he hadn't had any earache or giddiness and his hearing was fine. I carefully peeled off the paper and had to soak it off his left ear where it had stuck. This ear was very scarred and misshapen but there was nothing to suggest a skin tumour, and no sign of a bleeding point within the ear, so I asked him when the injury had happened.

"Somme, '16."

He then recounted the story. He was somewhere near or at the front line when he felt a blow on the side of his head and turned to his sergeant and asked what had happened.

"Beg pardon sir," had been the reply "They've blown your fuckin' ear off."

Dr R – THE HAND OF GOD

Night work in General Practice can occasionally be very rewarding but it is always exhausting because of the constant sleep interruptions. This certainly was worse for me as I got older. At around 2am one Sunday morning, I received a call from a distraught man reporting that his grandmother had died. He explained that she was 91 and her health had deteriorated significantly in the previous three months. It may come as a surprise to the layperson, but a call asking you to visit the dead is such a relief in the middle of the night, as one doesn't have to make a diagnosis and instigate treatment, all of which require one to be awake and alert. Confirming death, I can do in my sleep, so on this occasion I didn't bother to dress properly. I simply put on jumper and trousers over my pyjamas, popped on some trainers (no socks), and off I went. I duly arrived at a basement flat where I was shown into a dimly lit bedroom with "Granny" lying peacefully on her bed. She was surrounded by all the family: about eight in all. I squeezed by to have a look at the body, which was still warm but obviously very still. I got out my trusty stethoscope to impress everyone with my efficiency and placed it on her chest. I couldn't hear a heart, but I have to say I didn't try very hard because there wasn't much point. However, in the back of my mind always lurked the worry that I would send a misdiagnosed dead person off to the mortuary only for them miraculously to revive. When I worked in Casualty, we saw many comatose patients arriving in ambulances. A quick test to measure the level of unconsciousness was to vigorously rub the patient's chest with one's knuckles and measure the response on a scale of 1 to 5. I cannot remember the actual details. Without anyone seeming to notice, I applied the "knuckle-test" to her, at which she sat up abruptly. The family weren't the only ones to be shocked, but the old dear couldn't understand what all the fuss was about. It turned out this old lady was a much-loved person. The delight in the bedroom was palpable and it was all down to me! I had brought her back from the dead by just placing my hand on her chest. "The hand of God," I heard one daughter mutter in awe. I did mention to one of the relatives that the old lady might develop some slight bruising on her sternum in the next few days, (but hopefully no broken ribs, I thought). One of the children thrust two bottles of wine into my reluctant hands as I was leaving: quite a result, really. After that, I always carried a bottle bag in the boot of my car; you never knew when it might come in handy.

One Bank Holiday, Brighton Police Station called me out to a non-suspicious death in a basement flat in Brighton. I was busy dealing with live patients, so it took me a couple of hours to get there. On arrival, I found two happy policemen with their feet up enjoying a cigarette and clearly relieved not to be out there catching villains. The patient looked about 80, very dishevelled and surrounded by empty beer bottles. It looked as if he had fallen backwards over a rather grimy couch and was lying face up. It was quite dark in the room, with the only light coming from a rather ineffectual filthy 40-watt bulb. Fortunately, one of the bobbies lent me one of their powerful torches to shine over the poor chap. Even from three or four feet, he appeared to have been dead for several days, if not longer. Apparently, he lived alone so acquiring any sort of medical history wasn't going to be possible. As I have mentioned before, I have this paranoid fear that I'm going to declare someone dead only for them to wake up in the mortuary, which is enough to scare anyone to death! However, I guess the result would be the same and nobody would be any the wiser. Still, it's the principle of the thing. Just for a laugh and to lighten everyone's day up (well nearly everyone!), I grabbed the patient's wrist and declared, "Hey guys, I think I may have a weak pulse here." One of the police constables nearly choked on his cigarette, the other one appeared to be reaching for his truncheon. I think I was lucky to get out of there alive. No sense of humour, I thought.

Before a deceased person can be cremated, two medically qualified doctors must by law "sign them off" on a cremation form. This document has two parts. The doctor who signed the death certificate completes part 1, and another doctor is invited to confirm these details, externally inspect the corpse, and sign part 2. Both doctors were paid in cash by the undertaker for this task so there were never any complaints. There were some rumours going around that some of the medics (not me) forgot to inform the taxation authorities of this added income. These same shameless doctors (again, not me) often referred to this imbursement as "Ash

Cash". Disgraceful!

Anyway, I was asked to sign a part 2 on a cold, wet afternoon in February, and arrived at the undertakers rather miserable and dishevelled. I was greeted by one of the staff, in their warm office, dressed immaculately in the traditional morning suit, which I found rather galling. However, I had a mortgage to pay so I got on with it. I had arranged to meet the part 1 doctor to see the corpse for the last time. This particular medic, also known as "Mad Mary," duly arrived and lived up to her reputation. I was slightly bemused to see her reach for her ancient stethoscope and diligently search the patients' thorax of any evidence of the second coming! Satisfying herself that this frozen corpse was indeed lifeless, she nodded reverently for me to confirm her findings. The patient had been dead and refrigerated for at least seven days. I examined the poor man's wrist and once again declared that I thought I could feel a faint pulse. Although I found this prank hilarious, once again I was disappointed by the response. "Is it just me?" I began to wonder.

Dr D – THE NAKED TRUTH

Had I ever asked him I doubt if Stanley would have denied being bullied at school. I first met him when he was about 65, a short man with a limp and one almost useless arm, the result of birth trauma. Added to this he was not a good-looking man, his face dominated by an enormous nose separating two small pale blue eyes. His defence system was based on a razor-sharp wit, a confrontational sense of humour and clowning.

At our first encounter he complained that I was late and that the waiting room looked like a morgue, neither of which assertions was true, before introducing himself.

After he had described his medical problem, which he insisted on doing standing up, I told him I needed to examine his chest, then left the room briefly to collect a file from my secretary's office. I returned to find Stanley stark naked apart from his socks with one hand covering his genitals and the other obscuring his nose.

"What makes you think I'm Jewish, doctor?"

I soon got the measure of Stanley and always enjoyed the repartee.

"Doctor, you have a very attractive and charming secretary." These types of remarks were always delivered in a haughty accent.

"Indeed, I have."

"Have you seduced her yet?"

"No Stanley, I have not."

"I see, not yet, but none the less I fear I shall have to report you to the BMJ, (British Medical Journal), inform The Argus and break the news to your delightful wife."

"Very public-spirited of you Stanley. Have you come to see me for any reason other than blackmail?"

Stanley owned a small antique shop and pawnbrokers not far from his home in a large block of flats in central Brighton. I once called in on him just after visiting his wife.

"Ah, good morning doctor and welcome to my modest but well stocked emporium to which you have come, no doubt, to purchase an expensive trinket for your wife in compensation for your unacceptable behaviour; am I right?"

"No Stanley I am here to deliver your long-suffering wife's prescription that she hopes you will have the time and inclination to collect for her."

"Touché, doctor, touché."

Another much younger, rather excitable, patient who also seemed reluctant to sit down was JX. My consulting room was large, and he also used to pace up and down while we discussed his ailments. I believe his day job was in sales, but he was also a semi-pro musician, a piano player in the Elton John mode.

On one occasion, he rushed in saying he was in a hurry but had something interesting in his underpants he wished to show me, and he was right. In addition to two normal testicles, his scrotum contained another lump of about the same size, which was causing him no discomfort. With the aid of a pen torch, I demonstrated that, with the light behind it, it lit up like a pale red lamp bulb indicating that it was a fluid filled cyst and therefore almost certainly harmless. I told him it could be easily drained but might recur, in which case a surgeon could remove it.

"Oh no Duncan I don't want to get rid of it."

"That's OK; it won't do you any harm."

"That's reassuring, but that's not the point, I want to keep it."

"Why?"

"Well, it's a bit of a party piece, I call them my trollocks."

I didn't enquire as to what sort of parties he attended, but he had recently moved to Shoreham Beach!

Dr R – WET DREAMS AND LOST PROPERTY

To improve my consultation skills, I joined a counselling group of about eight local GPs. I learnt many secrets about my colleagues but was determined they were not going to find out much about me. This consisted of 10 sessions (all lasting about three hours on a Friday evening!) Halfway through the course, the counselling guru decided that we would study "dream therapy". Our homework was, if you were in the middle of a dream, you had to try to wake yourself up, or if you woke up spontaneously, you had to write down as much as you could remember on a handy notebook by the bedside. This was great fun learning about the weirdest dream and nightmares that my colleagues suffered from. Three weeks later, however, I was asked to share my dreams. Of course, I hadn't done any homework, so I made up a dream on the spot, as you do when you are caught out! "Well," I said. "I dreamt last night that I was windsurfing late one evening about an hour before sunset in the sea off Brighton on my own. It was a beautiful evening and I felt very content as I sailed further and further out to sea." Counsellor Guru, "I think we must stop right now Rod, as these are very clearly suicidal thoughts." The session was closed early so that I could stay behind for another tortuous hour of being debriefed! I needed to say something so offered another lie that things weren't too good at home. I never did own up; how could I?

The following day, the wind was blowing, the sun was shining, and all was well with the world. I rushed to the beach, rigged up my windsurf kit and was walking into the sea all pumped up with adrenalin, only to notice a young man walking into the sea with me, fully clothed. I shouted, "Hi, how's it going?" He said, "I'm going to commit suicide."

To my shame, looking at my watch, I actually said, "What? Now?"

"Yes, he said." It's difficult to have a sensible conversation with someone you don't want to, up to your waist in seawater and wearing a wetsuit. However, 15 minutes later, I had calmed him down, ascertained where he lived and negotiated that I would give him a lift back home now. Home turned out to be sheltered accommodation nearby. The very young nurse who answered the door was now looking at a fully clothed dried out male with a harassed irritable agitated middle-aged man in a pink and powder blue wet suit. I could see her eyes flicking from me to him, him to me, trying to work out who was the doctor and who was the patient. Anyway, all was sorted out and, feeling faintly pleased with myself, I rushed back to the sea. The wind had dropped along with my spirits!

Anna was dating a friend of mine and had recently moved into my GP practice area. She had decided to register with me. The thing is, I quite fancied Anna and had had one or two dances with her at a local nightclub before she joined my surgery. You must remember this was in the mid-1980s and I was very young, so I had not learnt the many pitfalls of General Practice. So, one afternoon, she turned up to tell me she was hoping to start a family and wanted to make sure everything was healthy from a woman's point of view. We had a bit of a chat about her past medical history, which had been uneventful, and she agreed to book in to see me at a later stage for a pelvic examination and cervical smear*. I didn't think any more about it until she turned up a couple of weeks later for her gynaecological appointment, at a moment when I was particularly harassed. After the usual preliminary chat, I asked her to pop up on the couch, pull the privacy curtain around her and undress as necessary. I asked her if she would like a chaperone, but she didn't think it was necessary. I finished writing up a few notes in her medical folder, and then went over to commence the examination. Anna hadn't bothered with the modesty curtain, and she was lying on the examination couch stark naked, which took me back a bit. Obviously, being professional, I didn't bat an eyelid, whatever that means! I proceeded to do a routine breast examination, and examined her abdomen externally, finishing up with an internal pelvic examination and a cervical cancer smear. This all went easily, and Anna appeared relaxed throughout the whole procedure: almost certainly more relaxed than me! I told her to get dressed in her own time while I filled in the paperwork. A few minutes later, she was back in the chair alongside my medical desk. I was quite pleased with how the whole consultation had worked out. However, this is when everything seemed to go wrong. I completed the necessary cancer smear forms, but the specimen was missing. I had mislaid the rectangular piece of glass that I had prepared Anna's smear on. It had simply disappeared! I searched all the obvious places and some less obvious and there couldn't be that many. Desperately, I asked her to look in her handbag and jokingly accused her of stealing it as a bit of a lark. However, all searches failed after a full five minutes.

I was becoming a bit bewildered to say the least and wasn't sure how to proceed. I didn't remember any lecture back at medical school on what to do in these types of circumstance – or maybe I just missed that nugget of information. Fortunately, Anna came to the rescue. She simply said, "Well Rod, we had better do it again," and in a flash was stark naked up on the couch once again. I felt it unnecessary to repeat the breast examination (although I was tempted), and just repeated the cervical smear. This time I didn't let go of the specimen until it was labelled and safely linked up with to the necessary form. I didn't even trust the hospital collection system, so I drove to the pathology laboratory personally after the surgery was over and delivered it myself.

I never did find the original specimen and at one stage, wondered if I had dreamt the whole situation. A few weeks later the report came back from the laboratory saying, "incomplete specimen, please repeat." You are joking, I thought, and I got the nurse to do it.

---

*I'm not even going to bother explaining what a "cervical smear" is as I'm pretty sure 99% of women and 1% of men are fully conversant with the term

Dr D – TWO JEWISH FUNERALS

Harold Pinter's mother was a petite, calm and rather shy but hospitable woman in contrast to her argumentative husband, also short but much feistier. During the war, he had exercised his power as a fire warden with a bit too much enthusiasm and graffiti appeared on walls in Hackney reading "Jack Bloody Pinter." This hadn't upset him in the least; he simply saw it as evidence of a job well done and he was equally proud of their son Harold's occasional displays of outrage. Early on in his acting career, before he became a playwright, Harold, after a day in rehearsal at The Royal Court Theatre, was standing in front of two men on the platform of Sloane Square Tube station. Their loud conversation was full of antisemitic remarks that Harold soon found intolerable. Confronting one of them, without a word, he punched him hard in the face. I suppose Harold looked sufficiently semitic for there to be no need, in true Pinteresque style, for dialogue.

Jack long outlived his wife, and I visited him regularly over 20 years, often coinciding with a visit from Harold who was a devoted and supportive son. He took me out to lunch on a few occasions and my wife and I attended a couple of his first nights. He remains one of the most impressive people I have ever met: very clever, very funny, and deeply committed to supporting the underdogs of life, worldwide.

When his father died, the funeral service was held in the small chapel in the Jewish Cemetery off Bear Rd in Brighton. Jewish funerals are, in my experience, refreshingly simple affairs. Jack had outlived all his contemporaries, so we were a small group of mourners who listened to the Rabbi chanting, reciting prayers, and then delivering a few words about the deceased before handing over to Harold who gave a predictably elegant eulogy for his father.

The grave, next to that of his wife, had been largely dug out by the gravediggers, but as custom demanded, Harold and I took off our jackets and laboured away for a few minutes shifting a few shovelfuls of chalk.

A few years later, I attended another funeral but with a larger turn-out. Maurice had run a couple of very successful menswear shops with the help of Rita, his second wife. She had no relatives and was not close to the children from his first marriage, so Maurice's death hit her very hard.

As the mourners left the graveside and headed for their cars, I lingered because I suspected she would be left on her own. Apart from one couple who went to put a stone on the nearby grave of a friend, this is exactly what happened. I waited until she felt comfortable about leaving and, as I held her arm, we walked slowly back to the main path, where we were joined by the returning couple. We passed the Pinter graves; just to break the silence I mentioned my connection.

"So, you know Harold Pinter."

"Yes, I knew him quite well."

The conversation stopped and, as we walked slowly on past the gravestones, I spotted the names of several old patients of mine.

Again, to break the silence I said to Rita that a lot of the people in the cemetery had been my patients.

"I'm not surprised," said Rita. "You're very popular in the Jewish community in Brighton, they trust you, and Jewish people always know where to go to for the best."

With perfect timing and intonation, the husband of our hitherto silent companions said softly "Maybe they could have done better."

It was at about this time that there was news in the press that Harold was seriously ill, so I wrote to him saying how sorry I was to hear of his illness, informed him that his parent's graves were tidy and recounted the story of my recent visit. A couple of days later I got a charming hand-written reply.

Two months later, he died, and we lost a brave man and the finest dramatist of his generation.

A few months after her husband's death Rita, who was struggling to cope with the absence of Maurice, developed a persistent headache; an X-ray examination confirmed that she had an unusual form of bone cancer involving her skull. There were only a couple of small, affected areas, no more being found on a scan of her entire skeleton. It was her oncologist's opinion that this was not an aggressive disease and that her prognosis was at least five years. Almost as if this diagnosis was welcome, she refused all treatment except analgesics and died in our hospice less than six months later, seemingly too sad to live on alone.

Dr R – COULD I HAVE DONE BETTER?

On an unusually quiet Friday evening when I was on call, Brighton Police Station rang to inform me that one of my patients was going "bonkers" (their words) in her flat and needed to go to the "funny farm" (not my words). Slightly annoyed with the policeman's turn of phrase, I explained that I was up to my eyes in emergencies and should be able to attend on Monday morning (about 60 hours later!) I was only joking, but obviously humour wasn't this officers' strong point; he was probably only 16 anyway. I did attend, about 30 minutes later. The patient's apartment was on the 23rd floor; thankfully the lift was working otherwise it would have been Monday by the time I got there! She had somehow smashed the lounge window and thrown some chairs out through the broken glass. If I had known this, I would have parked my car a little further away from the block. The worrying development was that she had been threatening to throw herself out. Now I was really worried about my car! The policeman attending was extremely young and deeply relieved to see me. The unfortunate lady, aged around 40, was clearly psychotic and a danger to herself and to others, including my precious vehicle. Sectioning her required two signatures: mine, and that of the duty psychiatric social worker. There was usually only one available over the weekend for the whole of the East Sussex area. It was looking like a very long night stretching out ahead of me. If I could calm her down sufficiently, I hoped she might agree to be admitted to the psychiatric unit voluntarily and then I could get some sleep. Fortunately, she did start to settle down, so I called for an ambulance. However, they informed me they would be up to 90 minutes, as there had been a major accident on the main road out of Brighton. Well, there was nothing for it but to offer her a lift personally to the hospital. (Never do this!) On the short journey, the patient was fumbling in her rather large purse for her cigarettes and asked me if I had a light. I didn't and said that I encouraged people not to smoke in my car anyway.

Five minutes later, I was safely handing her over to the duty psychiatrist, who happened to be a mate of mine. A few hours later, when I was fast asleep in my own bed, the phone rang again, this time from the hospital. My mate had apparently found a small handgun in my patients' purse and was asking why I hadn't mentioned it on the handover. I said that I had forgotten and hung up. My sleep was punctuated by several disturbing dreams that night.

I never gave a patient a lift to a hospital again.

Tamsin was booked in as an emergency at the end of a very busy Friday evening surgery. I had had enough, as I had been on call the previous evening and only managed to catch a couple of hours' sleep. I was exhausted and wired up on too many cups of coffee*. I quickly called my wife back home and suggested the family could meet up at our favourite Italian restaurant, about 45 minutes later, leaving me ample time to finish up at the surgery.

With one more patient to go, Tamsin walked in.

Her opening line was "Hello Doctor, I feel suicidal." Twenty minutes into the consultation I wasn't getting very far, so excused myself briefly from the room to make another phone call back home. "Better give me another 45 minutes, as I've run into a problem with one of my patients." All agreed, and back I went to Tamsin. I had got to know her well over the years, so, after another half an hour or so we started to get to the source of her feelings. As usual, it was boyfriend troubles. At the end of an hour, when all my staff and colleagues had gone home, I was confident that I could send her home to her folks for the night, as she still lived with them. I gave her my personal mobile phone number in case she needed to have a further chat during the evening. (Never do this!) I even offered to see her the next morning (Saturday) at around 10am, saying that I would come in especially.

"Oh, sorry Doctor, I can't make that," she said. "I've arranged to meet a girlfriend for breakfast and then go shopping." I gently, or perhaps, not so gently, reminded her that she had suicidal feelings. "Oh, I know Doctor, but life goes on doesn't it." Well, she was right there for both of us, and we individually set off on our various ways. I kept asking myself over the two hours of a very delayed supper whether that had been a successful consultation.

Not all consultations have happy endings, though. I had a lovely, harmless, schizophrenic patient called Kevin. Over the five years that I had known him, his condition always appeared to be well controlled; he held down a gardening job and lived with another schizophrenic patient of mine called Gill. Well, Kevin literally bounced into my consulting room to announce, "Hi Doc, I've never felt better. I'm off all my medication." I made a note of these two "encouraging" statements, had a brief chat about football and off he went on his merry way. I was later to learn that he had hung himself that night in his home while his partner was asleep. To this day, 35 years later, I still ask myself what I could have done to avert this tragedy. Perhaps encouraging him to restart his medication would have been a start.

One of my patients whose death I remember was a charming old man well into his 80s who I had seen from time to time over the preceding 10 years, although never with serious ailments. He was one of my favourite patients; I never rushed him because he was such good company and always had an interesting story to tell me. After we had sorted out what he had come for, I got up to see him to the door. As we were walking in that direction, he put an arm around my shoulder and said, "You are very good to me Doctor. You are just like a father to me." I was 40 at the time, a little less than half his age, but I was so chuffed. Ten minutes later, while crossing the road from the surgery premises to the supermarket, he was hit by a bus and killed immediately. I have to say I shed a few tears that evening when I was sharing the news with my wife. At least he didn't suffer some awful debilitating illness; he would have hated that. I was relieved that the last memory I had of him was that tender moment between us as he left my rooms. I often think of him, so he never really died for me.

*Decaffeinated coffee wasn't readily available then – I rarely drink anything else now. However, I have yet to manage alcohol-free wine and beers.

Dr D – PHOEBE

Claude Grahame-White was one of the UK's most famous aviation pioneers. In 1910, he was nearly the first person to fly from London to Manchester, in the Daily Mail-sponsored £10,000 challenge. However, his fellow competitor, a Frenchman called Louis Paulhan, beat him by flying through the night, which indicates that he was even more of a risk-taker than "Whitey" – as Phoebe, his second wife and latterly my patient, always called him.

Even in her 80s, Phoebe Lee was still a beauty, albeit a beauty with a very sharp tongue. She lived alone in one of the penthouses on top of the new Bedford Hotel, built on the site of the original hotel frequented by Charles Dickens. She had the daily help of a german housekeeper who continued to look after her for years, despite very rarely receiving any sign of appreciation.

Phoebe had had a tough early life. Her Jewish parents emigrated from Yorkshire to the US in about 1909 but, shortly after their arrival in New York, her father, who had earlier emigrated from Russia, died, leaving his wife with seven children, of whom Phoebe was the eldest. The middle five children were sent to an orphanage, but Phoebe stayed at home to help her mother care for the youngest child, Beatrice.

After leaving school in New York, Phoebe became a dancer; for a few years in the 1920s, she was in the Ziegfeld Follies and was part of an elite group including W. C. Fields and Jimmy Durante, who did comedy sketches for Ziegfeld and his friends in his private apartment.

Once, walking with a fellow long-legged hoofer from a rehearsal, they heard a man's voice behind them telling them to "sue the city, sue the goddam city."

At first, they ignored him, but he kept repeating his advice until they got to the end of the block and turned round to see that their advisor was a grinning dwarf.

"OK wise guy, why the advice?"

"You dames should sue the city" he said gravely "for building the sidewalk so far from your arses."

George Gershwin proposed to her, but he was rejected in favour of a Mr Harris who died before they could marry but left her comfortably off. She subsequently met the swashbuckling, wealthy Claude on a transatlantic voyage. They married in 1939 and, as far as I can tell, enjoyed an extremely successful relationship; they certainly lived in high style, complete with a large yacht and celebrity friends.

I don't remember Phoebe ever deigning to come to my surgery, but I made many visits to her flat. On one occasion, I accompanied her dentist on a visit to remove a loose tooth; my job was to administer a small dose of anaesthetic. My friend removed the tooth very skilfully and the patient woke up after no more than a few minutes in an atypically benign frame of mind.

"Oh, you are both SO handsome," she purred, before reaching out for her glasses.

After putting them on, she said, "Oh, perhaps not."

The lift stopped at the floor below her apartment. After walking up the stairs one morning, I was let in by the long-suffering Helga, whose greeting was drowned by the TV at full volume. I found Phoebe, who was by this time deaf, staring avidly at the screen image of Bette Davis. This must have been in about 1984, soon after Bette, who smoked 100 cigarettes a day all her life, had suffered a series of strokes that left her with a facial weakness that exaggerated those prominent eyes, which, on the screen, were surrounded by bright blue eye shadow below pencil thin arched eyebrows.

"Jesus Christ!" shouted Phoebe as soon as she saw me. "Looks like they just dug her up."

She did mellow a bit as she got older, and never complained about her failing health and strength. On one of my last visits, she presented me with a large box full of monogrammed red glasses from their yacht, "Majesta," as well as Whitey's signet ring, all of which I later presented to the museum set up in his honour at Hendon aerodrome. This was where his company had designed and manufactured aeroplanes, and he had been the test pilot for many aircraft there, between the wars.

Dr R – ROSEMARY'S BABY

I first encountered Rosemary when I had been in General Practice for five years. She was in her late twenties with three children, all girls. One was from her previous marriage; current partner was father to the other two. I saw her, I guess, about every two months, mostly with her youngest daughter, and with nothing particularly serious. When I did see her on her own, she was always turned out extremely well, but came across as concealing anxiety under a cover of self-confidence. It transpired that she was in an unsatisfactory relationship that she had been trying to escape from for several years. The partner was a rather intimidating man, part-time builder, and part-time crook, according to Rosemary. He had already served a custodial sentence for tax evasion. For five years in a row, Rosemary came to see me in my morning surgery on New Year's Eve. I noted that she was particularly agitated on these occasions, but I could never get to the bottom of why.

On the fifth visit, I asked her if she had anything planned for the rest of the day and that evening. She blurted out that, on New Year's Eve, she always went to Woodvale Crematorium in search of her lost baby. Then it all came out in a rush. Rosemary was the only child of her parents and had been brought up in a large four-bedroom terraced house in a very pleasant part of North-East London. She described her father as a successful gangster, but I cannot remember his specialty! On one occasion, she remembered the house being shot at from a passing vehicle, so a background of violence was the norm for her. As a child, she had wanted for nothing materially. However, from the age of about eight, her father had started to sexually molest her. This intensified after her mother died of cancer and they moved to live in the centre of Brighton. Rosemary, although clearly bright, hadn't done well at school and had become a loner with very few friends. What friends she did have were not close. At the age of 16, she became pregnant by her father but successfully concealed her plight until she was about 22 weeks pregnant, which was too late for a termination. Her father forced her into a relationship with a local boy who was far from intelligent. The pregnancy was thus conveniently blamed on the hapless youth. Her baby was delivered in one of Brighton's maternity units but was taken away from her after a couple of hours only for her to be told that her child had died. This all happened on the morning of New Year's Eve. She never saw her baby again, dead, or alive; but she knew it was a girl and she had named her Caroline. The "boyfriend" disappeared, and her father told her that her baby was buried somewhere in Woodvale burial grounds. Every New Year's Eve Rosemary would travel across Brighton and spent up to four hours searching the gravestones for the site of the grave of her first-born. A few months after leaving the maternity unit, she had quickly found a partner to move in with, partly to protect herself from the rapes of the father.

Rosemary's only information regarding her lost child was date of birth, place of birth, assumed name of Caroline (that she had requested), assumed surname, i.e., Rosemary's maiden name and not the boyfriend who had now run off, and the assumed burial grounds, Woodvale. Needless to say, her annual ritual search produced no results: only heartache. Rosemary felt that her anxious personality would be "cured" if she could only find the grave, so she could finally leave a cross of identification. I took it upon myself to have a go at finding this lost soul. This was in the late 1980s, so I thought I would go to the site office at the crematorium and see if they had records of all the graves on the site. Sure enough, there was a special area for young children that had very few gravestones. The records office produced a six-foot square board of double graves. Because of the lack of space, after a certain amount of time, a second baby/child was buried on to the top of the first but several feet less deep. The baby's grave was located on this fascinating chart of discoloured yellowing paper with feint ink names and dates of birth. Rosemary's baby was identified, and the very helpful administrator walked me up to the special site, which consisted of several hundred small mounds on the mown lawn. Every few yards there were numbered markers practically buried in the ground. It was a simple method of pacing out the yardage; and there she was after all those years. I was able to take Rosemary to visit her lost baby the following weekend. From then on, she could make as many successful pilgrimages as she pleased. Rosemary wasn't "cured", obviously, but at least it was partial closure for her. She now had one less demon to contend with. Her father had died several years before all this happened and knew nothing of Rosemary's subsequent findings. She wasn't able to forgive her father, just as he was never able to apologise to her for his behaviour even when he was quite old and feeble. Rosemary would visit him at least once a week, in hope. When he eventually died, she told me she had taken all her clothes off and laid down naked next to her dead father in bed.

She explained, "It was the only time in my life when I felt safe with my father."

Dr D – REPATRIATION

During the 1970s and early 1980s, I worked from a building in The Drive, Hove, owned by Nigel Porter, a very busy General Surgeon whose consulting rooms were on the first floor. In addition to being an exceptionally able surgeon, he was quite entrepreneurial. One of his business ventures was a company that provided travel insurance companies with doctors who were prepared to accompany people who had become seriously ill abroad, back to the UK. Most of these repatriation flights took me no further than European cities and Mediterranean resorts. However, on one trip, I went to New Orleans; and the longest was to Quito to bring home a Mrs Ayres, the mother of the First Secretary, to our embassy.

This unfortunate 80-year-old widow had suffered a major stroke as her plane was landing in Quito Airport, leaving her unable to speak and completely paralysed down one side of her body. Her son had been advised that the best treatment would be provided at the Military Hospital. However, Ecuador's army spent much of its time dealing with border skirmishes, so the hospital was well able to cope with battle injured young men, but not an 80-year-old stroke victim.

I find it impossible to stay awake on flights, so I got to Quito airport well rested. I was carrying about £3,000 in cash, money to pay for her hospital treatment. I had no trouble spotting a smiling Mr Ayres in the arrivals hall, as he was waving a large banner with the hand-painted greeting "Welcome to Quito, Dr Stewart "

An embassy car was waiting for us; when I explained that I was carrying the cost of her treatment in sterling, we headed off to change it into local currency. As we clutched each other to protect my cash, we probably looked like a recently reunited gay couple. Our destination turned out not to be a sturdy branch of Barclays but a glorified tent with a length of carpet for a door. We completed the exchange and headed back to the car with a wad of cruzeiros the size of a house brick. We were soon facing the hospital cashier, sitting in a well-fortified kiosk. The banknotes, of which there were many hundreds, were counted and recounted and finally the account was settled.

Mrs Ayres had been well nursed and had no pressure sores. She had been fed intravenously for three months; no real attempt had been made to mobilise her and there had been no improvement in her speech or swallowing. There might well have been none had she had been hospitalised in the UK, but her condition now made it reasonable for us to take her home.

I examined her and could find no reason to delay her repatriation, so we confirmed her passage and that of her accompanying daughter-in-law on the flight to Heathrow the following day.

Her son was exactly the type of person who should represent us abroad. A charming man, he had learned Spanish, and studied the country's history; I discovered him to be a mine of information about Ecuador's social, political, and economic situation.

Keen to show me round the city, Mr Ayres suggested we meet outside my hotel at 4am so that I could witness an Andean sunrise. We walked up through the deserted streets of the old town to the central square and the cathedral built by the Spanish and consecrated in 1572. The sunrise was truly spectacular, as was the interior of the cathedral, every square inch of which was gilded.

The ambulance taking us through the city later in the day was driven by a man determined not to let the fact that most of the inhabitants were enjoying their siesta prevent him from driving at great speed through traffic-free roads with bells and sirens at full volume.

Seats had been removed at the back of the plane to make room for Mrs Ayres, who was lying on a gurney next to a window; sadly, her stroke had also removed her vision on one side, and she could not see what was going on inside the plane.

The head stewardess was very attentive; soon after take-off, she asked Mrs Ayres, who had been offered only sips of water for three months if she would like a drink. Would she like a glass of sherry? She nodded vigorously and some sherry appeared in a glass, which her facial weakness would have prevented her from drinking. The apologetic stewardess took it away and returned with a very large measure of sherry in a highball glass with a bendy straw. I propped my patient up and made sure her good hand had a firm grip on the glass before returning to my seat. The gurgling sound of a straw being enthusiastically sucked soon had me back at the side of my patient who had just imbibed a third of a bottle of Cream Sherry in less than a minute.

On the basis that any self-respecting middle-class lady of her age could probably cope with a small sherry overdose without serious risk, I removed straw and glass, regained my seat and we all slept for about eight of the 15 hours on board. Mrs Ayres arrived home in good shape, despite my inattention.

I alternated making these trips with my friend and partner David Cairns. He had a much bigger problem on a flight from Rio de Janeiro, accompanying an old man with severe respiratory incapacity who needed positive pressure oxygen administration but desperately wanted to die at home. A careful estimate was made of the volume of gas he would require, excluding the plane's usual supply. All went well until, halfway across the Atlantic, it became obvious that the gas supply was inadequate, because the mechanism that delivered the gas was powered by the pressure of the gas.

The pilot was not pleased to hear that they would have to land in Lisbon to take on more cylinders.

"Do you have any idea how much it costs to make an unscheduled landing in an aircraft of this size?" He screamed at David, who wisely did not reply.

"Twenty thousand pounds, and I'll make sure they send the bill to you."

David had a few sleepless nights. However, in the end, all went well. The patient died in his own bed; and British Airways used the story in an advertising campaign designed to show what a caring organisation they were.

Dr R – MY AUNTIE

I have been prevaricating as to whether it would be wise to share this story with a cynical reader who might conclude that my integrity was compromised. However, in the end, I felt that the vast majority would feel that sometimes an innocent man can become unwittingly immersed in a situation that made him look very guilty.

I had been on a two-week family holiday in the sun and had returned to General Practice ready to fire on all cylinders. As was my habit on returning from a vacation, I would go into the surgery a couple of hours before my first appointment to catch up with any mail that hadn't been dealt with in my absence. Usually, an hour before "kick off", one of the receptionists would come in to make sure everything was in place, so at least the first few minutes after opening the doors to the public would run reasonably smoothly. This particular morning, one of my most trusted receptionists was on duty. We will call her Jane.

Jane, a single parent in her late twenties, was extremely bright with a very quick wit, despite an inadequate education.

"Any problems while I was away, Jane?" Maybe I was secretly hoping the practice would have collapsed into chaos without me to steady the ship.

"Not really, Doctor, "she replied, "it's been pretty quiet." After a rather theatrical pause she went on to add, "Oh yes. There was one rather enjoyable incident, but you probably wouldn't be interested."

"Probably not," I replied, but she ploughed on regardless with a poorly disguised twinkle in her eyes.

"Mandy from Moulsecoomb (a notorious and often dangerous council estate) rushed into a packed waiting room last Monday morning and screamed at the top of her voice; 'Doctor Brooks is shagging my Auntie', then she went out as quickly as she came in:"

"Bloody Hell Jane, you are joking?" I exclaimed.

"Why would I joke about something as serious as that?"

"Um, well, yes of course Jane, quite right. So, what did you do?"

"What could I do, Doctor, she was gone in a flash."

"I don't suppose you know whether any of the waiting patients heard, do you?" I was beginning to feel quite unnerved by this revelation.

"I don't think anyone had any choice, Doctor. In fact, it became quite a talking point after she had gone."

I was beginning to feel quite sick, and the memory of my lovely holiday was receding into the distance. Hoping against hope, I enquired as to whether any of my partners in the practice had heard the commotion.

"I don't think so Doctor. Did you want me to report it to them?"

'No, I fucking don't you silly cow' raced through my cerebral cortex and hurtled down my brain stem to the muscles in my tongue*. However, I managed to gag back this response at the last synapse and substituted it with a rather croaking: "Oh, I wouldn't bother them with it, Jane. They have got enough on their plate without having to deal with silly trivia like this."

"Oh, I don't think that they are that busy Doctor, after all, you did tell us you did most of the work in the practice. But if you are absolutely sure, Doctor?" she bounced back at me, her face loaded with sly menace.

"Yes, I am absolutely certain, Jane." I retorted with all the calmness I could muster. "I'll let you get on Jane. I don't want to hold you back, but before you go, have you any idea who this mythical Auntie is?"

"Oh yes Doctor, she is one of your regular patients, her name is 'X'. In fact, let me check your list for the afternoon. Ah, I thought so; she is the last patient seeing you at the end of this evening's surgery."

A sinking heart is a very accurate description of that feeling. In addition, my heart was plunging into my boots. Auntie X, much to my relief, never turned up and I never actually saw her again. Maybe she and her niece joined a neighbouring practice, only to haunt another unsuspecting innocent G.P.!

Unfortunately, the story did not end there. Two weeks later, when I was feeling that the proverbial dust was beginning to settle, and the smirk on Jane's face every time I looked at her was finally fading, I received a phone call from the Auntie's ex-partner. He had clearly got wind of this ridiculous accusation and wanted to discuss it with me. We will call him "Gary". Although he was not a patient of mine, I knew of him. A stocky man in his 40s, he was a builder by trade, and a part-time crook. He had an interesting history. Born in Brighton, he was married and lived in a Moulsecoomb council house where he kept himself busy fertilising his wife. Ten children later, after a two-year sentence for tax fraud he left his wife and teamed up with Auntie X, with whom he had two more children. They parted company a few years later and somehow, he had come to blame me for her decision to leave him. For reasons I am still not clear about, I agreed to meet up with him one evening in a rather dingy public house in Hove to discuss his delusion. I suppose I wanted, finally, to "put this story to bed", (perhaps not the most appropriate phrase in the circumstances!) After a ten-minute pleasant conversation, all seemed to be going well until he announced, much to my horror, that he felt £3,000 would make the story go away. Unsurprisingly, my relationship with him took a sudden turn for the worse. I have never been blackmailed before, nor since, I might add, but I suppose there is still time as my life is not over yet! I declined his offer, obviously, and left soon afterwards in dread of what was going to happen next. I had a feeling that Gary wasn't going to leave the matter alone.

Sure enough, a fortnight later, just as I was beginning to sleep a little easier again, Gary turned up on my doorstep, very drunk. My wife, Rachel, answered the door as I was in the bath at the time, but I could hear the conversation. Gary was making all kinds of accusations about me and threatening to take the story to the Sun newspaper. My wife, to her great credit, announced calmly that this didn't propose a problem, as we "didn't take The Sun."

This obviously did the trick, as I never heard from him again. I learnt several years later that he had died of a brain tumour, so I guess this whole, threatening saga was finally put to rest.

If any reader of this story has been, or is being blackmailed, then I wish them well.

*Clever medical speak for metaphorically "biting my tongue".

Dr D – RETIREMENT

I can well understand the frustration felt by people just trying to do their job but having to cope with the vagaries of human behaviour which so often cause delay and distraction. Fortunately, I was always fascinated by the absurdities, vanities, obsessions strengths and weaknesses that form a unique personality.

Confront these attributes with the stress of illness anxiety or a demanding life experience and many outcomes are possible.

All the strands in our life experience have an impact on how we react and as a GP trying to understand a patient's problems and needs, having access to as much information as possible, gained largely through the privilege of confidential conversations puts one in a powerful position to be helpful and effective. But much is lost if the doctor's only interest is confined to reaching a diagnosis. Compassion, humour and simply listening all enrich the experience for both parties and add to the benefits of a consultation.

Even now 14 years after hanging up the stethoscope, cancelling the medical defence insurance premiums and saying goodbye to patients, staff and colleagues never a week goes by without someone asking me for advice which I am more than happy to provide but usually after a bit of research. So, a vestige of those busy days remains for which I am grateful.

Looking back, I realise that I was lucky to have chosen a career which suited my interests, my temperament and my independent nature at a time when these attributes were more acceptable than they are today.

However, no doctor works in isolation, and I owe a great deal to my secretaries, practice nurses and fellow medics all of whom were very supportive in what is by any standards a very demanding job. My family also deserves a plaudit for putting up with an often-preoccupied parent/husband. I do feel guilty that my children might have had a better childhood.

GPs often do not provide the ultimate opinion; patients need the expertise of specialists and investigations. Recognising the point at which that need arises only comes with experience and erring, one hopes, on the side of caution.

The pandemic has significantly widened the gap that had already formed between doctor and patient in many practices and it concerns me that the traditional, and I would consider safe, model of primary care is becoming too fragmented and impersonal to provide the shared information for safe and effective treatment. On the other hand, the astonishing advances in imaging techniques, blood chemistry, genetics and therapeutic options undreamed of 40 years ago have improved statistical outcomes in some areas. Technology has displaced much of the intimacy and humour that created the events we present in this book. Our stories are concentrated more on the comedy than the tragedy of medical practice because we are seeking to amuse so we make no apologies for being more inclined to amuse than educate, not that these are irreconcilable outcomes? I should add here that all our stories are true so there is no point in suing us!

I was touched by seeing over 400 of my patients at my retirement event at which I handed over my practice lock stock and barrel to my successor. Retirement provided more time for my favourite pursuits which include working at our local hospice, Martlets. My first role was as the token medic on the board of the home care company. I barely spoke for the first year, committees were foreign territory for me, but I gradually learned the ropes and am now a board trustee.

One hospice patient, a GP, medical journalist and an old friend spent his last days in the in-patient unit where he was very well cared for. At the last of my visits he drifted out of his sedated sleep, greeted me warmly and thanked me for offering to conduct his funeral which was an offer I had not made but now felt unable to disown. I spent days trying to perfect my eulogy and the other spoken passages in what turned out to be a very well received humanist celebration of the very interesting life of this delightful man. Before he lapsed back into sleep, I warned him rather wimpishly that I had never done this before and wasn't entirely confident that I was up to the job.

"Oh, you'll be fine "he said cheerfully, and then enigmatically" and don't forget it will be the first time for both of us" Those were his last words to me, and he died peacefully 2 days later.

Dr R – RETIREMENT

I retired a few days short of my 48th birthday, following two major operations on my spine, after 17 years with the same practice. Being tall, a little under 6'3" in old money, and slim (then), I was prone to lower back pain following violent exercise – squash, without warming up, in my case. Warming down generally comprised slouching on a bar stool rehydrating with the club's finest lager! Things have moved on, I believe. However, following a surfing trip to North Cornwall, I developed what I could only describe as electricity shooting up my forearms when I clapped my hands together, so obviously I stopped clapping my hands and got on with my life. Three days later, while swimming, I noticed weakness of my left hand. I could not keep my fingers together on the downward stroke of the crawl. The situation appeared to have been solved by me stopping swimming. The next morning, however, I felt rubbish and wasn't fit enough to go to work. Coincidentally, I had seen a neurosurgeon, Mr Carl Hardwidge, the day before I had swanned off to the West Country. I had been moaning about a recurrence of low back pain, and he had ordered an MRI scan of my lower spine. On my return, I was able to ring this amiable chap and he took my symptoms very seriously. He was able to arrange an MRI scan of my whole spine the next day, and he met me straight after the investigation to go over the results for himself. He found a major disc prolapse at the level of C3-4 (high in the neck), a moderate prolapse at the level of T`8-9, (mid chest) and smaller protrusions at C4-5 and C6-7 (mid neck). My clinical self-diagnosis was cancer of the prostate with multiple spinal bone secondaries. (A good chum of mine, and not much older than me, had already died of this rotten illness). The neurosurgeon's bet was on acute multiple sclerosis. Thankfully, we were both wrong as with a bit of plumbing (or probably a lot), it could all be fixed, or so I hoped. Two days later, the prolapsed disc was sucked out and replaced with sterile bovine bone. I wished I hadn't told anyone about the actual procedure, as they went on and on about the probability of me developing "Mad Cow Disease". As it was the spine, I thought they would operate from the back of the neck, but they went through the front and side instead, with the surgeon's knife dangerously close to my thorax (windpipe), oesophagus (gullet) and the cervical artery and jugular vein (the main blood vessels carrying blood to and from the brain). All went swimmingly, and the symptoms in my upper limbs disappeared, leaving me with a rather macho wound across my neck, the sort of laceration one would expect to suffer while breaking up a knife-fight in the surgery waiting room! I was informed that the prolapse at T8-9 wasn't going to go away so five weeks later I was under the knife again, this time for 10 hours. I required a left lateral thoracotomy and a surgical pneumothorax, (opening the chest and deflating the lung), just so they could get a view of the protrusion. My eighth thoracic rib was binned; I would have liked to have kept it and pickled it in formalin. This would then have been sealed in plastic so that I could display it on a prominent shelf at home for all to see and admire; and more importantly, it would demonstrate once and for all what a brave chap I was. This wasn't to be, and I didn't want to make a fuss, although I did, and still do have a sneaky feeling that it was fed to the surgeon's dog.

I was off work for a total of five months; when I returned it was like starting all over again. All the sick patients I had deserted had either been cured or passed away. Either way, life was reasonably manageable to start with. However, as the pressures built up, the pain on the lower back of my right side and the whole of my right leg became quite severe, only made just tolerable by a copious quantity of analgesics. I was either in a lot of discomfort or doped up on painkillers, a potential recipe for a disaster. I was becoming very grumpy and short-tempered with my patients. Nobody seemed to be as ill as me, and I longed for my bed at the end of each evening surgery. Unfortunately, I was left with what is called a "Brown-Sequard Syndrome". The bottom line was chronic pain only partially controlled with an array of various analgesics. I lasted only five weeks back in General Practice before I resigned, never to return. My last day as a working GP was one I will never forget. I was getting progressively more ragged, and demoralised by exhaustion and persistent pain, with burning extending from my right loin area to the sole of my right foot. It was a Thursday, and I had fully booked morning and afternoon surgeries with extras, and on-call for the practice from 7 am to 7 pm, mopping up all emergency visits. During the afternoon surgery (which I could not wait to get finished, as all I could think of was my bed and something strong to dull my discomfort), I had three telephone calls requesting home visits, all of whom I managed to give what I thought to be sound advice over the phone. I had instructed all three patients to ring back if they felt there was a deterioration or needed to talk again, hoping against hope that this would be after 7 pm, when I would be safely tucked up in bed.

General Practice is an odd vocation. A completely booked three-hour surgery can take three hours or five hours, more like the latter. On this afternoon, the surgery "collapsed" with several "failure to attend" patients (for which I was eternally grateful), and several requiring certificates for flu-like illnesses (of which I was forever suspicious, but I wasn't a policeman). I thus had an unexpected "free" hour before I was off duty so decided to visit the three patients I had given advice to earlier in the afternoon. The first two patients had mild viral illnesses, so my previous phone advice had been sound. However, the third patient was a lovely old lady living alone in her 80s; on examination, she was clearly in distressing heart failure. I sent her into hospital. I later learnt that she had done very well but had required two weeks' treatment before she was judged fit to return home. I don't think this uncomplaining lady would have disturbed the "good doctor" again that night and would in all probability have not survived until the morning,

I went home and decided on the spot to resign that night. I informed one of the partners that I wouldn't be attending the surgery again. It made me feel I was en route to killing someone through negligence, and then there would be a complaint and then a hearing etc, etc. I decided to jump before I was pushed. The last thing I wanted was some awful complaint hanging over me, especially one I couldn't defend myself against. Interestingly, my pain symptoms reduced quite considerably once all the stresses of being a doctor were gone forever. It turned out to be a sound decision as, in the following three years, I had no less than three more cervical disc prolapses operated on, all "plugged" with bone taken from my iliac crest (hip bone). I also had bilateral ulnar nerve releases around my elbows, the area known colloquially as the "funny bone"; not that I found it faintly amusing! All my neurosurgical procedures were performed in the same ward of the same hospital by the same surgeon and the same anaesthetist. This was of enormous comfort to me, as I had great confidence in the hospital team. I was even slightly miffed that I didn't have the same bed every time, but I got over it.

During my 17 years in General Practice, I had a lot of fun with colleagues and staff alike. The staff were very streetwise, mostly female with a mixture of full-timers and part-timers. One of my partners agreed (not in writing, mind you), that when we had both retired from the practice, we would reveal to each other ALL our closely guarded secrets of what we had got up to in our careers as GPs and beyond. This led to us planning to set up The Old and Grey Club. We approached the other three partners to see if they were interested in joining but they couldn't be tempted. The reader must draw his or her own conclusions from this lack of co-operation. It was vital that neither member of "The Club" should die in service, but obviously, this was largely out of our control.

As it happened, we both retired from General Practice in our late forties, for different reasons, so neither of us was particularly old nor grey. As the naming of The Club wasn't meant to be literal, this wouldn't provide a stumbling block. To make it more fun and to widen it out a bit we decided to invite several hand-picked female receptionists to come along to our 'Grand Opening'. We thought perhaps they might like to provide a few stories of their own. To facilitate the meeting, I booked a table in a noisy Italian restaurant so that we would blend in. Transport was arranged so there would not be any excuses to avoid alcohol. Towards the end of a jolly evening, we divulged information regarding the general concept of our two-man club and suggested that it might be of mutual interest if we all partook in an "around the table truth session." The format would be to offer up a "secret" in turn; as a show of good faith, the good doctors would start things off. Much to our horror, it appeared there was absolutely nothing that the girls didn't already know about us. It was also blatantly clear that, at the end of the evening, we were no nearer finding out any scandals about them. I have to say I was pretty shocked about my ex-partner's revelations! It turned out to be a very expensive evening as these girls could hold their drink as well as their tongues a lot better than us!

I never regretted the decision to resign as I learnt just in time that an ill doctor simply cannot practice medicine safely. Chronic pain is all-consuming, and I feel very blessed that I am able to manage it without endangering anyone's life; although the friends I play golf with would find it difficult to back up that statement!

Duncan's Gratitude

"Never in the field of human
conflict was so much owed
by so many to so few."
WINSTON SPENCER CHURCHILL. 1940

"Never in the field of human
contact has one person owed
so much to so many."
DUNCAN BERNARD STEWART. 2023

Let me start with my first wife Sue and our two adored daughters Amy and Sophie, my brother Keith, Fran and all her family whose love and support I treasure.

Many colleagues and friends have contributed enormously to the pleasures of my long and rewarding life with their wit, wisdom and many kindnesses.

I was lucky enough to employ a succession of attractive, generous and efficient women who were wonderful practice managers. Gay, Sara, Barbara, Anne and Pauline. I hope I expressed my gratitude for the skill with which they organised the practice, coped with my inefficiencies, laughed at my jokes, stopped me from making a fool of myself and their extraordinarily kindness to our patients.

The patients, many thousands of them, who put their trust in me and often rewarded me by getting better, without whom there would be no stories to tell. I offer my sincere apologies to those I failed.

I would like to thank Ashley Hutchison for the excellence of his cover design and Rod's stepson Carl for his contributions to it. Rod's wife Louise has been a great support and has worked very hard on our behalf.

Our copy editor and proof-reader Hugh Barker has transformed our original document into a readable book with great skill. A pig's ear has become a silk purse.

I would also like to thank Andrew Popkiewicz and Peter Bridgewater for their help and Hugh Dawson for his encouragement.

Finally, I must thank Rod himself for suggesting we write this book together and for the good-humoured cooperation we have enjoyed.

Rod's Gratitude

"Imagine all the people"
JOHN LENNON - 1971

"How could I forget"
RODERICK JOHN BROOKS - 2023

Let me start with my first wife, Heather, who bore two lovely boys, Ben and Matthew, one of whom sadly died before reaching the age of 30. My second wife, Rachel, blessed me with another son, Freddie, and an extremely talented stepson, Jason. My third wife contributed with 2 more stepsons. My fourth, present and definitely my last wife Louise, of the past decade, has given me a stepson, Carl, who, much to my joy, has become a very loyal friend. All these women and boys (now young men) I am grateful to in many different ways as they are all part of my history.

Studying for and practicing as a doctor was a wonderful experience. I am deeply indebted to all those who contributed, whether large or small, to that particular journey.

My 17 years in General Practice was glued together by a succession of full-time and part-time young female receptionists. These women largely learnt on the job and were extremely bright.

Of the many, I have to flag up 3 special ones: Corinne, Julie, and Carole, whose friendship I still deeply value some 30 years after leaving General Practice.

As for the patients. Many will have passed away by now but none of them are forgotten because each individual enriched my life in a myriad of ways. I am very grateful to them all.

I would also like to thank Martin, Trevor and the team at Gemini for their much appreciated expertise.

Ashley Hutchison and my stepson, Carl, have made excellent contributions to the cover design of our book. My wife Louise, has worked tirelessly typing up my hand-written scribbles, correcting my appalling spelling and giving me unlimited support.

Lastly, I must thank Duncan for agreeing to my offer of writing a book together. I was only joking at the time, now I am stuck with him! A funnier man you would be pushed to meet.

DUNCAN STEWART studied Medicine at Guy's Hospital Medical School, surprised many by qualifying in 1967 and then moved to Brighton where he spent 18 months as a junior hospital doctor proving his unsuitability for a career in hospital medicine before heading for the unruliness of local NHS General Practice.

His first practice was an "in at the deep end" experience which lasted for the two years it took for the two partners to realise that a large practice with two surgeries and a list of well over 3000 patients living throughout the Brighton and Hove area was not sustainable. After an entirely amicable parting of the ways, he was invited to join a private GP practice and was pleasantly surprised to find that he quickly overcame any innate aversion to private medicine. He thoroughly enjoyed the work for the next forty years. Private practice was not particularly lucrative, but it did confer the luxury of spending more time with the patient. Woody Allen noted that 90% of success was "being there" to which Duncan would add that having got there, take your time as time is a great aid to survival for both the patient and the doctor.

In 1985 Duncan set up his own single-handed practice in Wilbury Road Hove and worked there until he retired in 2010 aged 66.

Duncan still lives in Brighton, loves the city, and now lives with his wife Fran in a seafront flat in Kemp Town. He has no dog, no beard and not many regrets.